$19.95

The Naval Institute Guide to

MARITIME MUSEUMS OF NORTH AMERICA

Pete Snieckus
71 valley view ave.
~~2 meadowbrook ct.~~
Summit NJ 07901

908-522-0661

please call if found – this book was really hard to find!
thanks . . .

Alaska
Yukon Territory
Northwest Territories
British Columbia
Alberta
Saskatchewan
Manitoba
8
8 Pacific Northwest
British Columbia
Yukon Territory
Washington
Oregon
Washington
Montana
North Dakota
Min
Oregon
South Dakota
7
Idaho
Wyoming
7 Central
Manitoba
North Dakota
South Dakota
Nebraska
Kansas
Oklahoma
Nebraska
Nevada
Utah
Colorado
Kansas
California
9
Oklahor
Arizona
New Mexico
9 West Coast and Hawaii
California
Hawaii
Texas
Hawaii

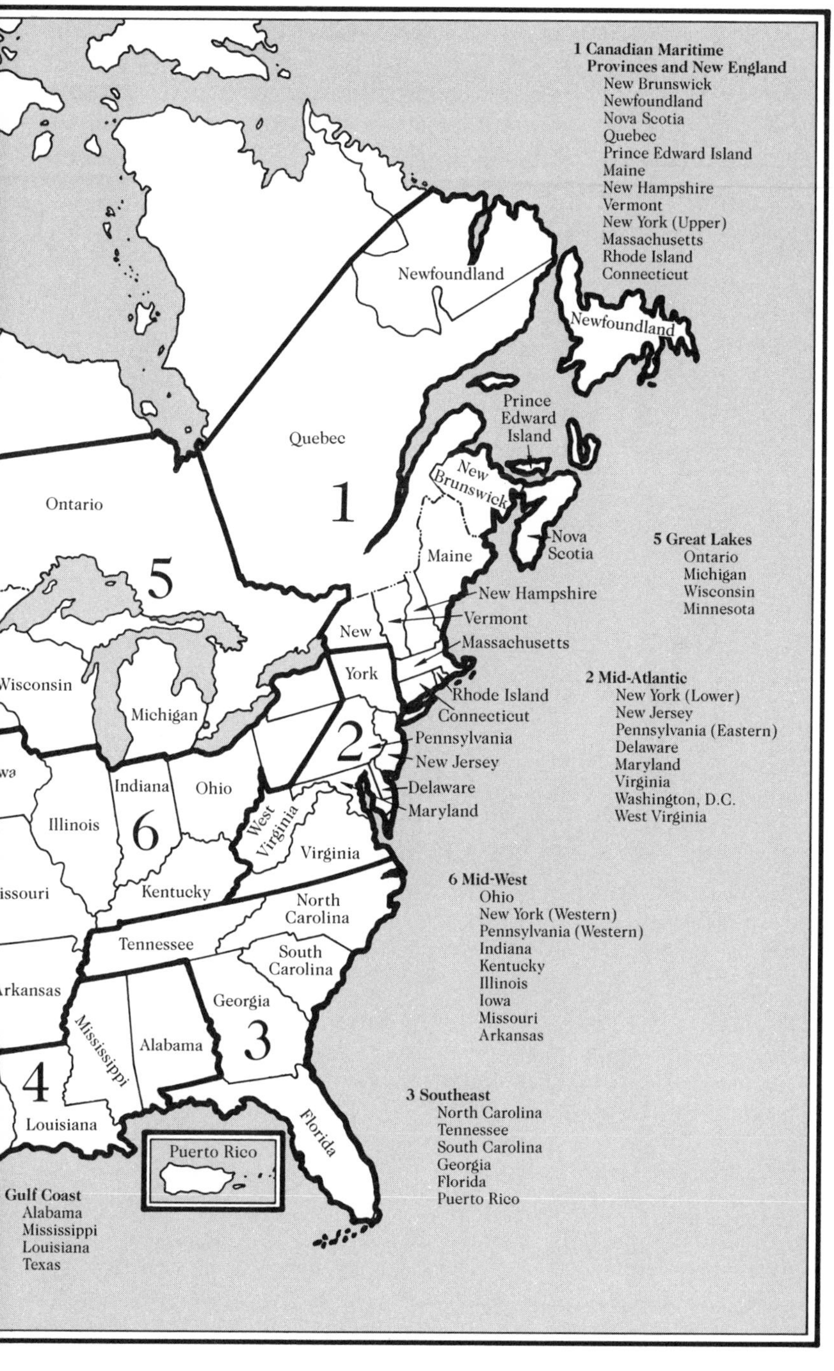
1 Canadian Maritime Provinces and New England
New Brunswick
Newfoundland
Nova Scotia
Quebec
Prince Edward Island
Maine
New Hampshire
Vermont
New York (Upper)
Massachusetts
Rhode Island
Connecticut
5 Great Lakes
Ontario
Michigan
Wisconsin
Minnesota
2 Mid-Atlantic
New York (Lower)
New Jersey
Pennsylvania (Eastern)
Delaware
Maryland
Virginia
Washington, D.C.
West Virginia
6 Mid-West
Ohio
New York (Western)
Pennsylvania (Western)
Indiana
Kentucky
Illinois
Iowa
Missouri
Arkansas
3 Southeast
North Carolina
Tennessee
South Carolina
Georgia
Florida
Puerto Rico
Gulf Coast
Alabama
Mississippi
Louisiana
Texas
Newfoundland
Quebec
Ontario
Prince Edward Island
New Brunswick
Nova Scotia
Maine
New Hampshire
Vermont
Massachusetts
New York
Rhode Island
Connecticut
Pennsylvania
New Jersey
Delaware
Maryland
Wisconsin
Michigan
Indiana
Ohio
Illinois
West Virginia
Virginia
Kentucky
North Carolina
Tennessee
South Carolina
Arkansas
Georgia
Mississippi
Alabama
Louisiana
Florida
Puerto Rico
1
2
3
4
5
6

The Naval Institute Guide to

MARITIME MUSEUMS OF NORTH AMERICA

With Selected Lighthouse,
Canal, and Canal Lock Museums

Naval Institute Press
Annapolis, Maryland

Robert H. Smith

Library of Congress Cataloging-in-Publication Data

Smith, R. H. (Robert H.)
The Naval Institute guide to maritime museums of North America: with selected lighthouse, canal, and canal lock museums / Robert H. Smith.
p. cm.
Includes index.
ISBN 0-87021-640-6
1. Naval museums—United States—Guide-books. 2. Naval museums—Canada—Guide-books. 3. United States—Description and travel—1981- —Guide-books. 4. Canada—Description and travel—1981- —Guide-books. I. United States Naval Institute. II. Title.
V13.U5S45 1990
387′.0074—dc20 90-6425
CIP

Printed in the United States of America on acid-free paper ♾

9 8 7 6 5 4 3 2

First printing

Cover photographs (clockwise from upper left): The Elissa *(iron bark), Galveston, Texas (courtesy of the Galveston Historical Foundation); Old Point Loma Lighthouse, Cabrillo National Monument, San Diego, California (courtesy of the National Park Service); the* W. P. Synder, Jr. *(steamboat), The Ohio River Museum, Marietta, Ohio (courtesy of the Ohio Historical Society).*

Cover design by R. Dawn Sollars

To Jenner, Derek, and Drue—may they share in the exploration of the world in their own way and with verve

CONTENTS

LIST OF MUSEUMS BY REGION

1. CANADIAN MARITIME PROVINCES AND NEW ENGLAND

2. MID-ATLANTIC

3. SOUTHEAST

4. GULF COAST

5. GREAT LAKES

6. MID-WEST

7. CENTRAL

8. PACIFIC NORTHWEST

9. WEST COAST AND HAWAII

LIST OF ILLUSTRATIONS

FOREWORD

The American merchant marine (that is, our nation's privately or publicly owned commercial ships) has been on the decline ever since Horace Greeley's famous statement "Go West, young man, go West" was current. Only ten major passenger liners have been built in America for the North Atlantic since the Civil War—a stunning illustration of how sad this phase of our maritime activity has been. Since World War II ended, our coastal merchant fleet has declined to such an extent that today it is devoid of virtually every ship type except oil tankers.

All is not lost, however. Coastal passenger shipping is being restored to life slowly, thanks largely to men like Luther Blount of Warren, Rhode Island, with a few overnight passenger ships in service today up and down the Atlantic coast flying the American flag. The great *Mississippi Queen* is doing very well, along with her historic companion, the beautiful and much loved *Delta Queen*. Best of all, our harbors and rivers are being infused with a string of fine new excursion boats, party boats, dinner boats, and the like. This is one real hope for the future.

Another reason to hope is that the nation seems to be growing aware of the importance and excitement of ships in our history. Witness this splendid new edition of *Smith's Complete Directory to Maritime Museums and Selected Lighthouse, Canal, and Canal Lock Museums*. Published by the Naval Institute Press as the *Naval Institute Guide to Maritime Museums of North America,* this imposing compendium is by far the largest and most complete effort of its kind. Not only does it list by region, with many useful particulars, a tremendous number of established and new maritime historical displays throughout North America, but it is also attractive and has two comprehensive indexes: one by name of museum and one by subject (which lists such things as Halls of Fame and even gift shops). The work is certainly going to become a standard reference, and it is clear evidence of a reawakening of interest in things maritime in the United States and Canada, something most welcome to those who have bemoaned the negative developments of recent years.

As curator of one of the museums included in this guide, I have found that the story of America's maritime past provokes an appreciation of the vital importance of merchant ships to our security and comfort today. My favorite theme when showing people around the American Merchant Marine Museum is that merchant ships need only a coat of gray paint to become vital war auxiliaries. And my choice word of warning to the innocents who throng through our lovely old mansion/museum is that without merchant ships, any future conflict involving the United States will have to be waged on our own land. This fact, as a rule, brings my listeners up sharply. It is a true, frightening fact. A study of history will show how vital merchant ships have been to America in the past. And an understanding of how frail our present merchant fleet is, is a message that can be hammered home via visits to the vast network of maritime museums all over our nation. This book will light the way for those who wish to make the journey.

Frank O. Braynard, Curator
American Merchant Marine Museum
Kings Point, New York

PREFACE

The main highway to North America was the Atlantic. It brought the Vikings, the English, the Spanish, and the Portuguese. It brought the Pilgrims, the dissidents, the visionaries, the thinkers, and the doers. In addition, the Spanish and English explored the Pacific coast of North America.

Settlements were established in the Maritime Provinces and New England, where the Gloucester fishermen flourished. Their culture and skills—shipbuilding and dory building—provided a vast quantity of seafood as well as whale oil, whale bone, and a variety of other by-products.

But they didn't stop there. The new settlers forged their way west, exploring rivers and lakes and settling along their shores. Fields were prepared for planting. Government and industry grew, paving the way for trade—both east and west—across the Atlantic and Pacific highways. Soon, lake steamers, followed by riverboats, were built to move people and commerce across the Great Lakes and up and down the great rivers.

As industry prospered, power was needed. Coal was the best and cheapest source, but to move it required water. Canals—even viaducts to carry the barges over land and water—were sculpted out of the landscape to move this important power source to the center of industry. The canal era lasted only four decades, however, as the development of railroads quickly took over the transportation of coal and freight.

Wars were waged and battles fought on the Great Lakes as well as on the seashores and rivers. A heritage of naval warfare began to emerge, and the ships and boats used in those early years are now being reclaimed yearly. Thousands of people have recognized, quite independently, the need to preserve as much of that maritime history and heritage as possible in order to pass on the knowledge of our forebears, highlighting the lure, agony, and romance of the sea and its ships.

Scattered throughout North America are many maritime museums. Each offers a historical experience: a piece of scrimshaw, a work of art, a navigational instrument, a ship model, a riverboat, a whaler's harpoon, a lighthouse to guide the mariner, a sea captain's home, a fisherman's dory, the excitement of a "Nantucket Sleigh Ride," and much, much more. Credit must go to all those dedicated individuals who have committed their time, talent, and financial resources to the preservation of the maritime adventure.

It gives me great pleasure to have compiled this guide of active maritime museums, large and small, as well as selected lighthouse, canal, and canal lock museums. Take the opportunity to explore as many as you can. In a lifetime, you cannot hope to see them all.

Thank you maritime preservationists, restorationists, and volunteers, one and all.

The Naval Institute Guide to

MARITIME MUSEUMS OF NORTH AMERICA

The *Star of India,* built on the Isle of Man in 1863 as the full-rigged merchant ship *Euterpe,* embarked on a career of hauling general cargo and transporting emigrants from London to New Zealand. In 1901 she entered the Alaska salmon industry, where her rig was changed to a bark. In 1906 she was renamed the *Star of India,* and in 1926 she was acquired by San Diegans to preserve her link with their maritime heritage. Now one of the vessels in the Maritime Museum of San Diego, the *Star of India* sails each summer. (Photo: Jerry MacMullen Library, Maritime Museum of San Diego.)

ONE

CANADIAN MARITIME PROVINCES AND NEW ENGLAND

NEW BRUNSWICK, CANADA

GRAND MANAN

Grand Manan Museum and Walter B. McLaughlin Marine Gallery

Grand Manan Museum and Walter B. McLaughlin Marine Gallery
P.O. Box 66
Grand Harbour, Grand Manan
New Brunswick E0G 1X0
Canada
(506) 662-3524

Location
Take I-95 to Bangor, Maine, exiting onto SR-9. Follow SR-9 ninety-five miles into Calair, Maine, where you exit onto Rte. 1. After approximately twenty-three miles, turn onto Rte. 785 toward Blacks Harbour. The museum is located in Grand Harbour, Grand Manan Island, roughly nineteen miles off the coast of Maine in the Bay of Fundy, a thirty-mile (two-hour) ferry boat ride south from Blacks Harbour.

Highlights
Maritime history

General Information
Founded in 1967, the Grand Manan Museum and Walter B. McLaughlin Marine Gallery exhibits a collection of local history and geology; the "Moses" collection of birds of Grand Manan Island; and a new marine gallery that investigates the history of local fishing. In addition, navigation, shipbuilding techniques, commerce, and shipwrecks are depicted through the use of marine charts, paintings, photographs, and artifacts. The lens and mechanism of the old Gannet Rock Lighthouse (1825–1880) are also on display.

Activities
Summer nature school during July and August

Admission
No entry fee, but donations accepted. Open daily, 10:30 A.M.–5 P.M., 15 June–Labor Day.

HOPEWELL CAPE
Albert County Museum

Albert County Museum
Albert County Historical Society
P.O. Box 3
Hopewell Cape
New Brunswick E0A 1Y0
Canada
(506) 734-2003

Location
Hopewell Cape is on Rte. 114 (the Tidal Trail), midway between Moncton and Fundy National Park. The museum is in an old jailhouse on the west bank of the Petitcodiac River.

Highlights
Local historical items

General Information
Albert County Museum, founded in 1957, is a "Museum in a gaol" (former county jail built in 1845). In addition to the "dungeon," mineral samples, and early furnishings, the museum contains maritime exhibits.

Many wooden sailing ships were built in Albert County. Among them was Rear Admiral Peary's *Roosevelt*, the ship that carried him on his successful and historic voyage in 1909 to discover the North Pole. Models and photographs of these wooden ships and the plans and tools used in building them are on display here.

Admission
Entry fee. Open Monday–Saturday, 10 A.M.–6 P.M., Sunday, 10 A.M.–8 P.M., 15 June–mid-September.

SAINT JOHN
New Brunswick Museum

New Brunswick Museum
277 Douglas Avenue
Saint John, New Brunswick E2K 1E5
Canada
(506) 658-1842

Location
The museum is situated on Douglas Avenue just five minutes west of downtown Saint John. Coming from the south on Rte. 1, take the Catherwood exit to Raynes Avenue, then turn north onto Douglas. If you're coming from the north, exit at Mills Street, then turn west onto Douglas.

Highlights
New Brunswick history
Natural sciences
Ship models
Scrimshaw

General Information
The New Brunswick Museum was founded in 1842 and displays objects of the natural and human history of New Brunswick and the Atlantic region.

Marine collections include half models, navigational instruments, shipbuilding tools, ship carvings, scrimshaw, ship models, and ship portraits.

Admission
Entry fee. Open daily, 10 A.M.–5 P.M., May–August; Tuesday–Sunday, 10 A.M.–5 P.M., September–April.

SHIPPAGAN
Aquarium and Marine Center
(Centre Marin de Shippagan)

Aquarium and Marine Center
(Centre Marin de Shippagan)
P.O. Box 1010
Shippagan, New Brunswick E0B 2P0
Canada
(506) 336-4771

Location
Reached by traveling north on Federal Highway 11 and Local Highway 345, the center is located near the northeast end of Gloucester, New Brunswick, overlooking the Bay of Chaleur.

Highlights
A new aquarium, the "touch-tank," where visitors can touch the aquatic life
Gift shop

General Information
Shippagan (the Micmac Indian word for "passage of ducks") Aquarium and Marine Center is a fascinating complex that explores the underwater life and world of fishing in the Gulf of St. Lawrence, which is home to many fish species. From the powerful wolffish with its threatening jaw to the graceful lumpfish, you will meet typical local fish in more than thirty tanks. Over 800 slides and a twenty-minute commentary reveal the stormy history of fishing in the Gulf, the waters of which have been the object of many revelries and much greed from the twelfth century to modern time.

An ultramodern wheelhouse equipped with electronic instruments (some of which operate while visitors watch), makes one realize the importance of electronics for today's commercial fishermen. A computerized map provides visitors with valuable information on the fisheries in the Gulf of St. Lawrence. Gears, photographs, and diagrams complete the exhibition on fisheries and fishing techniques.

Activities
Audiovisual presentation on the fishing industry of the Gulf of Saint Lawrence, and restoration of a 1904 lighthouse (with access to tower)

Admission
Entry fee. Open daily, 10 A.M.–6 P.M., May–September.

NEWFOUNDLAND, CANADA

MUSGRAVE HARBOUR
Fishermen's Museum

Fishermen's Museum
4 Marine Drive
Musgrave Harbour, Newfoundland A0G 3J0
Canada
(709) 655-2162

Location
Ferry to Port Aux Basques from North Sydney, Cape Breton Island. Take Rte. 1 north by northeast approximately 300 miles to the intersection of Rte. 330. Bear north about 36 miles on Rte. 330 into Musgrave Harbour on the coast of Hamilton Sound.

Highlights
Artifacts reflecting life of fishermen in the area
Ship models
Books, newspapers, pictures, and more

General Information
The Fishermen's Museum is housed in a building designed by Sir William Coaker, founder of the Fishermen's Protective Union. Collections include: items pertaining to fisheries; ship models, such as miniature fishing boats; engines; photographs; logbooks from the lighthouse (built circa 1902) that contain accounts of local shipwrecks.

Activities
Conducted tours

Admission
Entry fee. Open daily, 8 A.M.–5 P.M., June–mid-September.

ST. JOHN'S
Newfoundland Museum at the Murray Premises

Newfoundland Museum at the Murray Premises
c/o Newfoundland Museum
283–285 Duckworth Street
St. John's, Newfoundland A1C 1G9
Canada
(709) 576-5044

Location
Follow Rte. 2 to the Harbour Arterial on Water Street in St. John's.

Highlights
Maritime history

General Information
The Newfoundland Museum at the Murray Premises, founded in 1983, exhibits marine history, natural history, and military history components of the Newfoundland Museum's collection. Included are exhibits on underwater archaeology, navigation, cartography, sea disasters, and the evolution of sea trade from the sixteenth-century Basque whalers to early twentieth-century fish merchants.

Activities
Education and public programs

Admission
No entry fee. Open Monday–Friday, 9 A.M.–4:45 P.M., Saturdays, Sundays, and holidays, 10 A.M.– 5:45 P.M., year-round.

NOVA SCOTIA, CANADA

CENTERVILLE
Archelaus Smith Museum

Archelaus Smith Museum
Archelaus Smith Historical Society
c/o McGray Post Office
Centerville, Nova Scotia B0W 2G0
Canada
(902) 745-2411/3361

Location
Cape Sable Island is about 155 miles southwest of Halifax. The museum is located in Centerville, roughly three miles south of the junction of Rtes. 3 and 330 across the Cape Sable Island causeway.

Highlights
Boatbuilding
Fishing industry

General Information
The Archelaus Smith Museum, founded in 1970, exhibits artifacts that pertain to the marine involvement of the community such as the fishing industry and boatbuilding. Other displays include artifacts from shipwrecks and works by local artists that illustrate the history of Cape Sable Island and genealogical information.

Activities
Research projects

Admission
No entry fee. Open daily, 9:30 A.M.–5:30 P.M., 15 June–late September.

HALIFAX
Maritime Command Museum

Maritime Command Museum
Canadian Forces Base Halifax
Halifax, Nova Scotia B3K 2X0
Canada
(902) 427-8250

Location
The museum occupies Admiralty House, which lies between North, Gottingen, Russell, and Barrington Streets, five blocks north of Citadel Hill in Halifax.

Highlights
History of the Royal Canadian Navy
Library

General Information
Founded in 1974, the Maritime Command Museum is located in Admiralty House, which was built between 1814 and 1818. This Georgian style house first served as the official residence of the commander in chief of the British North American Station. Over the years it has been used as a summer residence, a hospital, and a wardroom.

The main objective of the Maritime Command Museum is to collect, preserve, and display the artifacts and history of the Canadian Maritime Military Forces. The museum maintains a library and archives relevant to naval history and the dockyard since 1759. It also houses a permanent collection displaying the history of the Royal Canadian Navy, which was founded on 4 May 1910.

Activities
Guided tours

Admission
No entry fee. Open Monday–Friday, 9:30 A.M.–3:30 P.M., September–June; Monday–Friday, 9:30 A.M.–8:30 P.M., Saturdays, Sundays, and holidays, 1 P.M.–5 P.M., July–August.

Maritime Museum of the Atlantic

Maritime Museum of the Atlantic
1675 Lower Water Street
Halifax, Nova Scotia B3J 1S3
Canada
(902) 429-8210

Location
The museum overlooks the waterfront on Lower Water Street in Halifax.

Highlights
The CSS *Acadia* (retired Canadian hydrographic survey vessel built in 1913)
William Robertson and Son Ship Chandlery
Ship models and thirty-five small craft
"Age of Steam," "Navy Shipwrecks," and "Lifesavings and Days of Sail" galleries
Library (4,000 volumes)

General Information
Maritime Museum of the Atlantic, founded in 1948, exhibits nautical history through a wide range of marine artifacts, from ship's hardware (as exhibited in the turn-of-the-century ship chandlery)

to over thirty-five small craft and an 846-ton steamship, the CSS *Acadia,* Canada's first purpose-built hydrographic survey vessel.

The museum also has nearly 100 ship models, a large collection of navigational instruments, and shipwrights' tools. Its research library contains over 4,000 titles, 15,000 photographs, and a small collection of vessel plans.

The museum is the marine history branch of the Nova Scotia Museum. Together with the Fisheries Museum of the Atlantic in Lunenburg, it collects, preserves, and interprets the material culture of the marine history of the Atlantic provinces.

Activities
Regular programs on the collection, a special program on oceanography, and research associates

Admission
No entry fee, but donations accepted. Open daily, 9:30 A.M.–5 P.M., except Tuesday (9:30 A.M.–8 P.M.) and Sunday (1 P.M.–5 P.M.), 1 November–May; daily 9:30 A.M.–5:30 P.M., except Tuesday (9:30 A.M.–8 P.M.) and Sunday (1 P.M.–5:30 P.M.), 15 May–31 October. CSS *Acadia* open 1 June–Labor Day.

HANTSPORT
Churchill House and Marine Memorial Room Museum

Churchill House and
Marine Memorial Room Museum
P.O. Box 101
Hantsport, Nova Scotia B0P 1P0
Canada
(902) 684-3461

Location
Churchill House is located in Hantsport, forty-two miles north by northwest from Halifax (just beyond Windsor) on Rte. 101.

Highlights
Churchill House and Museum
Ship models

General Information
The Churchill House and Marine Memorial Room Museum, founded in 1967, is housed in the home (c. 1860) of Ezra Churchill, a Nova Scotia shipbuilder. The Marine Memorial Room, overlooking the Avon River, takes the visitor back to early shipbuilding days when many a fine vessel was launched to sail the seven seas. At one time, Hantsport was rated fifth in the world as a builder of fine ships, a total of 120 ships having been built there.

Exhibits include shipbuilding tools, nautical instruments, old logs, ship models, and pictures.

Admission
No entry fee, but donations accepted. Open daily, 10 A.M.–noon and 1 P.M.–5 P.M., 2 July–1 September.

LA HAVE ISLAND
La Have Island Marine Museum

La Have Island Marine Museum
Bell's Island
La Have Island, Nova Scotia B0R 1C0
Canada
(902) 688-2565

Location
Travel sixty-six miles south of Halifax on Rte. 103. At the junction of Rte. 331, turn east toward Petit. Ferries run to and from the island.

Highlights
Maritime history

General Information
The La Have Island Marine Museum, founded in 1972, was previously a church and now houses a collection of marine artifacts.

Admission
No entry fee, but donations accepted. Open daily, 10 A.M.–6 P.M., July–August; Saturdays and Sundays, 1 P.M.–6 P.M., September.

LIVERPOOL
Queens County Museum

Queens County Museum
P.O. Box 1078
Liverpool, Nova Scotia B0T 1K0
Canada
(902) 354-4058

Location
Situated in the southwest tip of Nova Scotia, Liverpool is approximately eighty-five miles west of Halifax on Rte. 103.

Highlights
Shipbuilding history

General Information
Founded in 1980, the Queens County Museum is adjacent to the 200-year-old Perkin House and is designed to resemble the original buildings surrounding it.

The main gallery exhibit introduces Queens County through displays of its natural setting—land, rivers, and ocean. The exhibit demonstrates historically how mankind and nature have combined to yield the lifestyle of today's residents.

The museum collection of artifacts and records pertains to the history of residents and industries in the county since 1760; the development of local fishing, lumbering, and shipbuilding; and the period of the privateers. History buffs and genealogy enthusiasts will find the museum a worthwhile place to visit. The Queens County Historical Society maintains extensive archives.

Admission
No entry fee, but donations accepted. Open Monday–Saturday, 9:30 A.M.–5:30 P.M., Sunday, 1 P.M.–5:30 P.M. in summer; Tuesday–Friday, 1 P.M.–5 P.M., Saturday, 9 A.M.–5 P.M. in winter.

LOUISBOURG
Atlantic Statiquarium Marine Museum

Atlantic Statiquarium Marine Museum
1328 Main Street
P.O. Box 316
Louisbourg, Nova Scotia B0A 1M0
Canada
(902) 733-2220/2721

Location
Once on Cape Breton Island (northeastern Nova Scotia), take either Rte. 105 or Rte. 4 to Sydney, then travel south on Rte. 22 to Louisbourg. The museum is on the ground floor of a building (c. 1895) on Main Street.

Highlights
Early local fishery artifacts
Shipwreck artifacts
Ship models

General Information
The ocean embraces a rich world that, for the most part, remains hidden from our eyes by the restless surface of its water. It's a world full of secrets into which the Atlantic Statiquarium Marine Museum will give you a glimpse.

In this unique museum, founded in 1977, you will be pleasantly introduced to many creatures and objects from the local marine environment. See the recovered sunken treasure of *Le Chameau,* wrecked in 1725, and other historic shipwrecks of particular interest to divers and history buffs.

See also the exhibits featuring ship models, marine artifacts, and many items used by local fishermen until just a few years ago. Visitors can observe sea creatures and their behavior close-up at the saltwater aquarium. Their fossilized ancestors on display give evidence of life in the seas during times that even predate dinosaurs.

Activities
Reproductions in pewter

Admission
Entry fee. Open daily, 10 A.M.–7 P.M., June–September; 10 A.M.–9 P.M., July–August.

LUNENBURG
Fisheries Museum of the Atlantic

Fisheries Museum of the Atlantic
P.O. Box 1363
Lunenburg, Nova Scotia B0J 2C0
Canada
(902) 634-4794

Location
The town of Lunenburg lies approximately forty-four miles south of Halifax on Rte. 324. The museum is located on Bluenose Drive (at the end of Duke Street, just off Rte. 3) on the historic waterfront. A sister dory shop is located on Rte. 103.

Highlights
The *Theresa E. Connor* (schooner)
The *Cape Sable* (steel-hulled side trawler/dragger)
Dory shop
Aquarium
Gift shop/restaurant

General Information
The Fisheries Museum of the Atlantic, founded in 1967, has a collection that includes the *Theresa E. Connor,* built in 1938, the last of the salt-banking schooners to operate out of Lunenburg, and the *Cape Sable,* built in 1962, one of the freshwater fish draggers of the Lunenburg fishing fleet.

The five buildings, which were originally part of W. C. Smith and Company's fish operations, house exhibits dealing with the Atlantic Canadian fishing industry, including five inshore fishing vessels and an aquarium of fish representative of the types important to the industry; a documentation center; an education center; and a Canadian parks exhibit dealing with the Grand Banks fisheries.

A theater, gift shop, and restaurant are also on the grounds.

Activities
Films dealing with deep-sea and other fisheries; demonstrations of net mending and knot tying; fish splitting, bait-bag making, rope and wire splicing; hands-on participation in dory building; and information about lobsters.

Admission
Entry fee. Open daily, 9:30 A.M.–5:30 P.M., 15 May–31 October; Thursdays only, 9:30 A.M.–8 P.M., July–August.

MAHONE BAY
Settler's Museum

Settler's Museum
P.O. Box 181
Mahone Bay, Nova Scotia B0J 2E0
Canada
(902) 624-8021

Location
Mahone Bay lies approximately forty-four miles southwest of Halifax via Rte. 103.

Highlights
Ship models

General Information
The Settler's Museum, founded in 1978, contains a collection of materials used by the first settlers of the district: clothing, kitchen equipment, furniture, farm equipment, pictures, quilts, dishes, boots, and shoes, together with early shipbuilding tools and ship models from local shipyards.

Activities
Meetings, activity days, and lectures

Admission
No entry fee, but donations accepted. Open Tuesday–Saturday, 10 A.M.–4 P.M., Sunday, 2 P.M.–4 P.M., year-round

MAITLAND
Lawrence House

Lawrence House
c/o Nova Scotia Museum
1747 Summer Street
Halifax, Nova Scotia B3H 3A6
Canada
(902) 261-2628

Location
From Truro travel south/southwest on Rte. 102 to the junction with Rte. 236. Head toward South Maitland, then north about two miles into Maitland.

Highlights
Shipbuilding history

General Information
The Lawrence House, established as a museum in 1967, is located in the home of William D. Lawrence, designer and builder of the largest three-masted ship in Canada. Furnishings and memorabilia in the house relate to the Lawrence family and shipbuilding in the Cobequid Bay area. The house is both a national and a provincial historic site.

Typical of the grand homes of shipbuilders, shipowners, and captains, the Lawrence House was built about 1870 when Maitland and other towns in Nova Scotia were prosperous shipbuilding communities. In the early 1870s a number of vessels over 1,000 tons were being built; but Lawrence wanted to design an even larger one. In the fall of 1872 the keel was laid for a great ship, the *William D. Lawrence,* and with the assistance of his brother Lockhart as master builder, his son John as foreman, and a work force of seventy-five men, Lawrence began to make his dream a reality. On 27 October 1874 over 4,000 people flocked to Maitland to witness the launching of the 2,459-ton ship.

Activities
Tours

Admission
No entry fee, but donations accepted. Open Monday–Saturday, 9:30 A.M.–5:30 P.M., Sunday, 1 P.M.–5:30 P.M., 15 May–31 October.

MARGAREE HARBOUR
Schooner Museum

Schooner Museum
Shore Road and Cabot Trail
Margaree Harbour, Nova Scotia B0E 2B0
Canada
(902) 235-2317

Location
Travel north from Mulgrave on Rte. 19 approximately seventy-two miles to Margaree Harbour, Cape Breton Island. The museum is at the corner of Shore Road and Cabot Trail.

Highlights
The *Marian Elizabeth* (schooner)
Gift shops

General Information
Schooner Museum is located in the hold of the *Marian Elizabeth,* the last of the old saltbankers originally built without an engine in Lunenburg, Nova Scotia, in 1918.

The Museum features the crew's living quarters as well as photographs, a videotape, and other artifacts depicting the seagoing life of the fisherman in the early 1920s. It also highlights the *Marian Elizabeth*'s varied career, from her dory fisherman days when she transported her catch of salt cod from the Grand Banks to Portugal, to her time as a rumrunner along the eastern seaboard, to her coal-freighting days on the Newfoundland Lighthouse Run. She now houses a popular seafood restaurant on her deck (which also features piano music—only tunes from 1918 to 1958, the music that was in the air when she was a working vessel!). Just ashore are the Schooner Village Gift Shops and Coffee Shop.

Admission
No entry fee. Open by request 21 June–30 June and 1 September–15 October. Open daily, 10 A.M.–4 P.M., 1 July–31 August.

PARRSBORO
Ottawa House By-the-Sea

Ottawa House By-the-Sea
Shore Historic Society
Partridge Island
Parrsboro, Nova Scotia B0M 1S0
Canada
(902) 254-3266

Location
From Moncton, New Brunswick, take Rte. 2 east/southeast through Sackville into Amherst. Parrsboro lies about thirty-eight miles south of Amherst on Rte. 2. In town, follow Main Street to Partridge Island Road.

Highlights
Shipbuilding history

General Information
Ottawa House By-the-Sea, founded in 1979 as a museum, is the sole remnant of the original Partridge Island settlement. Once an inn, the house was built more than 200 years ago by James Ratchford, a prominent trader in the early history of Parrsboro. Ottawa House is devoted to the shipbuilding and maritime heritage of the area. Exhibits include a collection of shipbuilding tools, photographs of many of the important vessels launched from local yards, and artifacts from the days of sail. Rooms on the second floor reflect the home's appearance during Sir Charles Tupper's residency.

Activities
Museum tours

Admission
No entry fee. Open daily, 9 A.M.–7 P.M., July–Labor Day.

SHELBURNE
Dory Shop

The Dory Shop
Dock Street
P.O. Box 39
Shelburne, Nova Scotia B0T 1W0
Canada
(902) 875-3219

Location
Shelburne lies approximately 109 miles south of Halifax on Rte. 103. The shop is on Dock Street, an exit off of Rte. 103.

Highlights
History of dory building

General Information
The Dory Shop, also known as the John Williams Dory Shop, was originally established in 1880 as part of the dory-building industry which, at one time, included at least seven shops along the Shelburne waterfront. Thousands of dories were made and shipped all over the world. In 1877 Issac Coffin Crowell designed, patented, and built what was to become the famous Shelburne dory. Known for its exceptional strength, it was the dory preferred by Gloucester and other fishermen. John Williams served his apprenticeship under the guidance of Issac Crowell.

When the John Williams Dory Shop was in operation, both the first and third floors were devoted to the storage of lumber, while the dories were built on the second floor. A visitor to the dory shop would have seen a number of dories in various states of completion—an early version of the assembly line.

The Dory Shop was affected by the decline in dory production and ceased operations entirely in 1971. It was reopened in 1983 as a branch of the Nova Scotia Museum and is now operated for the museum by the Shelburne Historical Society.

Activities
Demonstration of dory building

Admission
No entry fee, but donations accepted. Open daily, 9:30 A.M.–5:30 P.M., July–31 August.

YARMOUTH

Yarmouth County Museum

Yarmouth County Museum
P.O. Box 39
Yarmouth, Nova Scotia B5A 4B1
Canada
(902) 742-5539

Location
Located on the southwestern tip of Nova Scotia, Yarmouth is approximately 192 miles south of Halifax on Rte. 103. Ferries leave from Portland and Bar Harbor, Maine. The museum is located at 22 Collins Street in downtown Yarmouth.

Highlights
Library
Bookshop

General Information
The Yarmouth County Museum contains in its exhibits and records a picture of the continuity of life in one of Canada's oldest seaport communities. Yarmouth was founded in 1761 by settlers from New England. Shipping and allied trades made the town prosperous in the nineteenth century, and in the 1870s it was Canada's leading seaport, per capita of population, in number and tonnage of sailing ships.

The museum's collection of ship paintings and models, the period rooms, costumes, and pioneer artifacts, all tell their own story for visitors.

The museum also boasts a research library and archive.

Activities
Historical Society meeting is held monthly

Admission
Entry fee. Open Monday–Saturday, 9 A.M.–5 P.M., Sunday, 1 P.M.–5 P.M., 1 June–15 October; Tuesday–Saturday, 2 P.M.–5 P.M., 16 October–31 May.

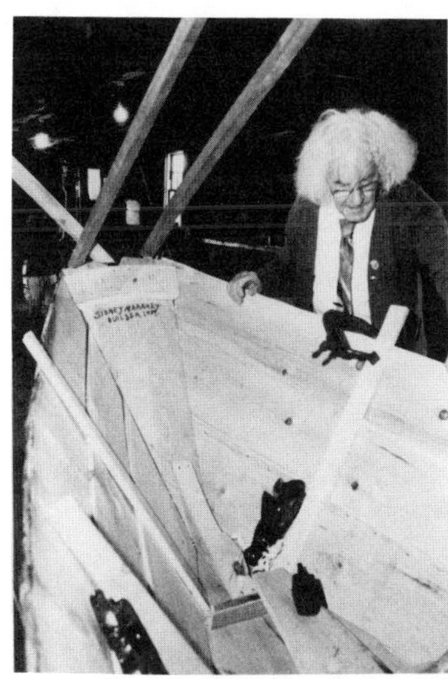

A Shelburne dory being built and on display at the John Williams Dory Shop, Shelburne, Nova Scotia. (Photos courtesy of the Shelburne County Museum.)

The sloop *Providence* is a reproduction of the Continental Navy ship that was the first war command of John Paul Jones. Originally built in 1775 to confront the British in Narragansett Bay, the sloop was commissioned the *Katy*. Later renamed the *Providence,* the ship was Rhode Island's initial contribution to the Continental Navy. (Photo courtesy of the Seaport '76 Foundation, Ltd.)

QUEBEC, CANADA

L'ISLET-SUR-MER
Bernier Maritime Museum
(Musée Maritime Bernier)

Bernier Maritime Museum
(Musée Maritime Bernier)
55 est, des Pionniers
L'Islet-sur-Mer, Québec G0R 2B0
Canada
(418) 247-5001

Location
Approximately sixty miles northeast of Quebec City, L'Islet-sur-Mer lies on the south side of the St. Lawrence River on Rte. 132.

Highlights
The *J. E. Bernier II* (sailing school)
The *Ernest Lapointe* (icebreaker)
Ship models and hovercraft
Library, gift shop

General Information
The Bernier Maritime Museum, founded in 1968, exhibits a collection that includes modern and ancient ship models; navigation instruments; lighthouse lenses and machinery; the wreck of the *Empress of Ireland;* the library and souvenirs of Captain Joseph-Elzear Bernier; wooden ships of the nineteenth century; tools, half-hulls, sails and rigging, and models; Saint-Lawrence schooners; preservation of the icebreaker *Ernest Lapointe* (1940), the hovercraft *Bras d'Or* (1968), the schooner *Jean Yvan* (1958), and the *J. E. Bernier II,* to be utilized as a sailing school; and displays of various traditional crafts used on the Saint Lawrence.

Activities
Guided tours, itinerant exhibitions, documentary films, documentation center, illustration of navigation on the Saint Lawrence River, and demonstration of ancient maritime techniques

Admission
Entry fee.
Museum: open daily, 9 A.M.–4:30 P.M., September–May; 9 A.M.–6 P.M., June–August.
The *Ernest Lapointe:* open June–August.

POINTE-AU-PÈRE
Rimouski Sea Museum (Musée de la Mer de Rimouski)

Rimouski Sea Museum
(Musée de la Mer de Rimouski)
1034 du Phare, P.O. Box 40
Pointe-au-Père, Québec G0K 1G0
Canada
(418) 724-6214

Location
"Father Point" is about five miles east of Rimouski on Rte. 132 (on the south side of the St. Lawrence River, approximately ten miles northeast of Quebec).

Highlights
The HMCS *Rimouski* (corvette, that is, a warship ranked just below a frigate)
The wreck of the *Empress of Ireland*
Lighthouse
Father Point Navigational Aid Center
The saltwater marsh of Pointe-au-Père

General Information
Because of its unique location at the frontier between inland waters and the maritime environment, Pointe-au-Père played an important historic role for more than a century. Because of its many navigational aid facilities and a St. Lawrence pilot station, it was well known to navigators by the beginning of the twentieth century. In 1976 the lighthouse and associated buildings were declared a national historic site.

Visitors may tour the lighthouse, the foghorn shed, the first keeper's house, and the exhibits on the HMCS *Rimouski,* a Canadian corvette that fought during World War II, and the *Empress of Ireland,* which sank off Rimouski on 29 May 1914 with a loss of 1,014 lives. Displays include original artifacts, montages, models, dioramas, and photographs depicting the maritime partrimony of the region.

Activities
Illustrations, exhibitions, educational programs, historical research, and preservation

Admission
No entry fee. Open daily, 9 A.M.–5 P.M., 29 May–5 September.

QUEBEC

Cartier-Brébeuf National Historical Park (Parc Historique National Cartier-Brébeuf)

Cartier-Brébeuf National Historical Park
(Parc Historique National Cartier-Brébeuf)
175, rue de l'Espinay, P.O. Box 2474
Québec, Québec G1K 7R3
Canada
(418) 648-4038

Location
You can reach the park (175, rue de l'Espinay) by heading north via Cote d'Abraham and rue Dorchester approximately two miles out from the city center.

Highlights
Life-size reproduction of *La Grande Hermine* (flagship)

General Information
The information center commemorates Jacques Cartier, first European known to have spent a winter in Canada (1535–36) and Jean de Brébeuf, a martyred Jesuit priest. The museum contains documents that illustrate Cartier's second voyage, the mixing of sixteenth-century European and American Indian cultures, and the initial implantation of the Jesuits in "New France."

The life-size reproduction of *La Grande Hermine*, the flagship of Jacques Cartier, contains an exposition in the mooring basin. Visitors may tour only the hull.

Activities
Guided tours of *La Grande Hermine*, hands-on display of navigation instruments, an audiovisual presentation entitled "The Grande Hermine," and maps and photographs illustrating the park's different themes. Special activities include a puppet theater and "Les Aquadimanches" (Nautical Sundays) every Sunday in July.

Admission
No entry fee. Call or write the museum for information about their opening hours.

Port of Quebec in the Nineteenth Century National Historical Site (Lieu Historique National le Port de Québec au XIXe Siècle)

Port of Quebec in the Nineteenth Century
National Historical Site
Lieu Historique National
le Port de Québec au XIXe Siècle
100, rue Saint-Andre, P.O. Box 2474
Québec, Québec G1K 7R3
Canada
(418) 648-3300

Location
The site is located at 100, Saint-Andre Street in the ancient cement works, and it is integrated into the harbor installations of the Louise Basin.

Highlights
The history of the Port of Quebec

General Information

The Port of Quebec in the Nineteenth Century National Historical Site, founded in 1984, exhibits illustrations of the development of the Port of Quebec and the evolution of the dockyards and the ships of the nineteenth century.

Mannequins in period costumes, models, three-dimensional structures, and sound tracks re-create the hustle and bustle of dockside Quebec. The "La chasse-galerie" (shooting gallery) slide presentation transports spectators to the legendary times of logging camps in the 1800s.

Also exhibited are reproductions of ships' bows, hulls, and shipbuilding tools; models; photographs and renderings; a temporary exhibition hall; and an observation deck from which to view the port and town of Quebec. This deck provides a magnificent view of harbor activities and the architecture typical of Old Quebec.

Activities

Guided tours, an audiovisual presentation entitled "Journey in a Flying Canoe," and a documentation center. Special activities include folk dancing and model builders at work.

Admission

No entry fee. Open Tuesday–Friday, 10 A.M.–noon, 1 P.M.–4 P.M., Saturdays and Sundays, 11 A.M.–5 P.M., March–April; Monday, 1 P.M.–5 P.M., Tuesday–Sunday, 10 A.M.–5 P.M., June–August; Tuesday–Friday, 10 A.M.–noon, 1 P.M.–4 P.M., Saturdays and Sundays, 11 A.M.–5 P.M., September–November; by reservation only, December–February except for Quebec Carnival Time (9–17 February, 11 A.M.–5 P.M.). Call for information.

PRINCE EDWARD ISLAND, CANADA

CHARLOTTETOWN
Green Park Shipbuilding Museum

Green Park Shipbuilding Museum
Port Hill, Tyne Valley (RR 1)
Prince Edward Island C0B 2C0
Canada
(902) 831-2206

Location
Ferry from Bayfield, New Brunswick, to Borden, Prince Edward Island. Take Rte. 1A west to Rte. 2. Follow Rte. 2 a short distance to the intersection of Rte. 12 east, which leads into Port Hill.

Highlights
History of wooden shipbuilding
Annual blueberry social

General Information
The Green Park Shipbuilding Museum, founded in 1973, is a re-created nineteenth-century wooden shipbuilding yard, an interpretive center, and a restored 1865 Victorian house.

Exhibits include carpentry and blacksmith shops, plus a partially completed full-size vessel.

Admission
Entry fee. Open daily, 10 A.M.–6 P.M., mid-June–mid-September.

MAINE

BAR HARBOR
Islesford Historical Museum

Islesford Historical Museum
National Park Service
Attn: Superintendent
101 Main Street
Bar Harbor, ME 04609
(207) 244-9224

Location
Bar Harbor is forty-six miles southeast of Bangor, Maine, on Mount Desert Island. The museum is actually situated on Little Cranberry Island, just south of there, approachable by ferry from both Northeast and Southeast Harbors.

Highlights
Maritime history

General Information
Islesford Historical Museum, founded in 1919, preserves a part of the history of maritime New England.

Admission
No entry fee. Open daily, 10 A.M.–5 P.M., mid-June–September.

BATH
Maine Maritime Museum

Maine Maritime Museum
243 Washington Street
Bath, ME 04530
(207) 443-1316

Location

Follow I-95 to Rte. 1. Head east one mile to Bath (thirty-five miles northeast of Portland on Boothbay) on the west side of the Kennebec River.

Highlights

The *Sherman Zwicker* (Grand Banks schooner)
Lobstering and the "Coast of Maine" exhibit
Maritime history exhibit building
Small-craft collection
The apprentice shop (wooden boatbuilding)
Long Reach Log (newsletter)
Library (6,000 volumes) on Maine maritime history

General Information

For centuries mariners have built wooden ships, sailed them to faraway ports, and fished from them on banks and bays for elusive cod and lobster. This rich seafaring heritage comes to life at the Maine Maritime Museum, founded in 1962. The museum includes a restored ten-acre shipyard—with over 1,000 feet of river frontage, it's the last shipyard intact in the country where sailing vessels were built—a boatbuilding school, a lobstering exhibit, and a new major exhibit on Maine's maritime heritage. Exhibits depict local shipbuilding families and traditions as well as regional history and models; half-models; tools; instruments; trade goods; seamen's possessions; small boats; and dioramas.

For exhibits on dory fishing, go on board the Grand Banks schooner *Sherman Zwikher* when she is in port. The shipyard also houses an apprentice shop where traditional boatbuilding skills are taught, exhibits on woodship construction, and a fine collection of small craft used along the Maine coast and inland waterways.

Activities

Two video presentations, training programs in small wooden boatbuilding, group tours by appointment, and an annual symposium on maritime history

Admission

Entry fee. Open daily, 9:30 A.M.–5 P.M., year-round. Closed national holidays.

BOOTHBAY

Grand Banks Schooner Museum

Grand Banks Schooner Museum
P.O. Box 123
Boothbay, ME 04537
(207) 633-4727

Location
See the Bath, Maine Maritime Museum listing for directions, as the schooner is docked there.

Highlights
The *Sherman Zwicker* (a 142-foot dory schooner)

General Information
Grand Banks Schooner Museum, founded in 1968, preserves and exhibits the *Sherman Zwicker,* a 142-foot dory schooner, as a significant representative of the area's fishing history. Completely restored and operational, this historic vessel is accessible both above and below decks to the viewing public. This is the only seaworthy vessel of this type that remains active in waterfront and Tall Ship activities, such as celebrations in Boston and New York City.

The engine room is particularly interesting: much of it is filled with the massive Fairbanks Morse 320-horsepower engine that drives the ship at a cruising speed of 9.5 knots.

Admission
Entry fee. (For information on their opening hours, see the Bath, Maine Maritime Museum listing.)

BOOTHBAY HARBOR

Boothbay Region Historical Society

Boothbay Region Historical Society
70 Oak Street
Boothbay Harbor, ME 04538
(207) 633-3932/3666

Location
At Bath, head east on Rte. 1 ten miles to SR-27. Boothbay Harbor is on the peninsula between the Sheepscot and Damariscotta Rivers and shares the peninsula and adjacent islands with a dozen other communities, including Boothbay (settled 1630), of which it was once a part.

Highlights
Maritime history

General Information
The Boothbay Region Historical Society is a nineteenth-century sea captain's residence. It is of Italianate design and period furnishings. The exhibits include implements of the fishing and shipbuilding industries, plus nineteenth-century household appliances, old photographs, and documents.

Admission
Entry fee. Open Wednesday, Friday, and Saturday, 10 A.M.–4 P.M., July–Labor Day; Saturday, 10 A.M.–2 P.M. in winter. Other times by appointment.

CAPE ELIZABETH
Portland Head Light

Officer in Charge
Portland Head Light
Cottage Road
P.O. Box 252
Cape Elizabeth, ME 04107
(207) 799-2661

Location
On Casco Bay, Cape Elizabeth is four miles south of South Portland, off Rte. 77. The head light is on the south side of the harbor entrance.

Highlights
Portland Head Light

Racing in the North Atlantic is the primary activity the Gloucester fishermen participate in. The *Gertrude L. Thiebaud* is shown here in a photograph taken in 1930. (All rights reserved; Rosenfeld Collections, Mystic Seaport Museum, Inc.)

General Information

Portland Head Light was erected in 1791 on orders from George Washington, after seventy-four shipowners petitioned for a beacon to guide them into Maine's busiest harbor. It was the first light authorized by the United States and is one of the oldest lighthouses in continuous use.

Henry Wadsworth Longfellow frequently hiked from Portland to compose under the tower. Waves swept away the 2,000-pound fog bell in 1869, deposited the ship *Annie C. McGuire* at the base of the cliffs in 1886, and smashed in the whistlehouse wall in 1973, knocking out the foghorn and temporarily extinguishing the light.

Portland Head Light is one of the most visited lights on the Atlantic seaboard. The tower's hurricane deck provides a view of more than 200 islands in the sweep of Casco Bay.

Admission
No entry fee. Park: open daily, sunrise–sunset year-round.
Lighthouse and museum: open daily, 8 A.M.–4 P.M., year-round.

CASTINE

Allie Ryan Maritime Collection

(*See also:* Maine Maritime Academy)

Allie Ryan Maritime Collection
of the Maine State Maritime Museum
State House Station 83
Castine, ME 04421
(207) 326-4311, ext. 254

Location
This collection is housed in Quick Hall at the Maine Maritime Academy, located on SR-199 in Castine.

Highlights
Maine/New England maritime history
Steamboat history
Ship models
Library (350 volumes)

General Information
Allie Ryan Maritime Collection details the importance of the steamboat through hundreds of paintings, lithographs, and photographs. A replica of the pilothouse from the steamer *Golden Rod,* an engine-room telegraph, and other materials are also here.

Exhibits include paintings, prints, broadsides, photographs, ship models, navigation instruments, main steam engine, steamboat pilothouse replica, ships' papers, steamboat line schedules, and brochures, plus a 350-volume library on maritime history.

Admission
No entry fee, but donations accepted. Open Monday, Wednesday, and Friday, 9 A.M.–noon and 1 P.M.–3 P.M. Other times by appointment.

Maine Maritime Academy
(*See also:* Allie Ryan Maritime Collection)

Maine Maritime Academy
The *State of Maine*
Castine, ME 04421
(207) 326-4311, ext. 254

Location
Thirty-eight miles south of Bangor, Castine lies on the east side of the Penobscot River. Take Rte. 1A south from Bangor fifteen miles to Prospect. Head east on Rte. 174 two miles to Urland, then south on SR-175/166 fourteen miles to Castine.

Highlights
The *State of Maine* training ship

General Information
Berthed at the Maine Maritime Academy dock is the *State of Maine,* a 13,300-ton training ship for academy students. The ship, the former USNS *Upshur,* was originally designed as a luxury passenger ship but was converted into a troop transport during the Korean War. It also saw service during the Cuban missile crisis and the Vietnam conflict.

Admission
No entry fee. Guided tours on the *State of Maine* when in port (usually July–April).

FRIENDSHIP

Friendship Museum

Friendship Museum
P.O. Box 321
Friendship, ME 04547
(207) 832-4221 (May–November, 832-4897)

Location
Friendship is approximately twenty-seven miles northeast of Bath. In Damariscotta turn south onto Rte. 130, heading toward Pemaquid Point. Continue one-half mile west of Friendship Village on Rte. 220 to arrive at the museum.

Highlights
Memorabilia of the town of Friendship

General Information
Friendship Museum was founded in 1964 and is housed in an old brick schoolhouse built in 1850. The museum contains exhibits on the community and the history of the sailing craft known as the *Friendship*.

Admission
No entry fee, but donations accepted. Open Tuesday–Saturday, 1 P.M.–4 P.M., Sunday, 2 P.M.–5 P.M., July–Labor Day.

GREENVILLE

Moosehead Marine Museum

Moosehead Marine Museum
P.O. Box 1151
Greenville, ME 04441
(207) 695-2716

Location
The museum is located in the center of Greenville, seventy-five miles northwest of Bangor at the south end of Moosehead Lake.

Highlights
The *Katahdin* (steamboat)
The *Katahdin Knots* (newsletter)

General Information
For many years before the opening of the road system in the United States, water traffic was the primary mode of transportation around the country, including the area around Moosehead Lake. Steamboats carried livestock, railroad equipment, supplies, and passengers. Steamboat history began there in 1836 with the steamboat *Moosehead.* Many of the boats were built at Greenville and the West Cove shipyard.

The Moosehead Marine Museum, founded in 1970, is a floating museum aboard the lake steamer SS *Katahdin.* Exhibits include artifacts and photos concerning the steamboat era on Moosehead Lake, logging, and the Mount Kineo Hotel, considered one of the finest resort properties in the world during its heyday. The museum has two rooms of area memorabilia: one room is devoted to the ships of the lake, the other to the great hotel era, the Mount Kineo in particular.

The SS *Katahdin,* a 1914 lake ferry steamship used on the last log drive in the nation, has undergone restoration and is once again carrying passengers on Moosehead Lake.

Activities
Head of lake cruises and Mount Kineo cruises

Admission
Cruises: Moosehead Lake—Monday–Friday, 10 A.M.–4 P.M., Memorial Day–30 September. Other times by appointment.

ISLESBORO

Sailor's Memorial Museum and Lighthouse

Sailor's Memorial Museum
Grindle Point
P.O. Box 76
Islesboro, ME 04848
(207) 734-2253 or 789-5611

Location
Take I-95 to Augusta, exiting onto Rte. 202. Travel east forty-six miles to Belfast, then south on Rte. 1 thirteen miles to Lincolnville. At Grindle Point board the auto ferry to Islesboro Island (or board the auto ferry at Lincolnville Beach).

Highlights
Lighthouse

General Information
Sailor's Memorial Museum, founded in 1936, contains collections that include maritime and other historic coastal artifacts and materials, primarily about local heritage. The Grindle Point keeper's house is also open to visitors.

Admission
No entry fee. Open Tuesday–Sunday, 10 A.M.–4 P.M., mid-June–Labor Day.

KENNEBUNK
Brick Store Museum

Brick Store Museum
P.O. Box 177
Kennebunk, ME 04043
(207) 985-4802

Location
Kennebunk lies twenty-five miles south of Portland on Rte. 1, one mile east of I-95. The museum is located downtown at 117 Main Street.

Highlights
Maritime history
Research library
Museum gift shop

General Information
The Brick Store Museum is a complex of four restored nineteenth-century buildings, including William Lord's brick store (1825). The museum contains changing exhibits of fine and decorative arts, historical and maritime collections, and a research library.
The Brick Store Museum also operates the Taylor Barry House at 24 Summer Street in Kennebunk. It is an elegant sea captain's home (1803) with an original stenciled hallway, period rooms, and an adjoining early twentieth-century artist's studio.

Activities
Architectural walking tours every Friday at 2 P.M., 10 June–14 October. Leaving from the Museum, the tours pass by homes (1760–1900) in the Kennebunk Historic District and end with a visit to the Taylor Barry House.

Admission
Entry fee for the museum and the Taylor Barry House. Open Tuesday–Saturday, 10 A.M.–4:30 P.M., year-round.

KITTERY
Kittery Historical and Naval Museum

Kittery Historical and Naval Museum
Rogers Road
P.O. Box 453
Kittery, ME 03904
(207) 439-3080

Location
Five miles north of Portsmouth, New Hampshire, off I-95 at Rte. 1 (by the traffic circle at Rte. 236) is an old sea town where ships have been built since its earliest days. Across the Piscataqua River is the Portsmouth Naval Shipyard.

Highlights
Geneaology of Kittery families and local culture
Changing exhibits
Ship models
Library

General Information
Kittery Historical and Naval Museum, founded in 1975, has assumed the responsibility of preserving and interpreting the history of the naval shipyard in Kittery and the closely related onshore activities.

Kittery, the Gateway to Maine and the state's oldest community, was first settled in 1623. From 1695 to 1749 three English warships were constructed by local craftsmen. In 1776 the first Continental naval vessel, the *Raleigh,* was launched on the Piscataqua. On 12 June 1800 the Department of the Navy purchased Seavey Island in Kittery and established the first government installation of its kind in the United States—the Portsmouth Naval Shipyard.

The museum exhibits objects and manuscripts on the history of the Portsmouth Naval Shipyard and the history of Kittery's shipbuilding industry. At the museum you will see a thirteen-foot model of the sloop *Ranger,* models of eighteenth-, nineteenth-, and twentieth-century naval vessels, a naval Gatling gun, photographs, dioramas, paintings of bygone days, ships' plans, and logs. Manuscripts are also available for researchers.

Activities
Special exhibits and events

Admission
No entry fee. Open Monday–Saturday, 10 A.M.–4 P.M., Memorial Day–15 October. By appointment only the rest of the year.

MACHIASPORT

Machiasport Historical Society

Gates House/Machiasport Historical Society
Route 92
P.O. Box 301
Machiasport, ME 04655
(207) 255-8860

Location
Machiasport lies about ninety-five miles due east of Bangor on Machias Bay. Take Rte. 1 to SR-92. The society operates the Gates House in town.

Highlights
Ship models
Library

General Information
The Gates House, built circa 1800, is a Federal-style house with several rooms furnished in period fashion. The maritime room exhibits include ship models and a maritime and genealogical library.

Admission
No entry fee, but donations accepted. Open Monday–Friday, noon–4 P.M., June–September. Other times by appointment.

NORTHEAST HARBOR
The Great Harbor Collection Museum

The Great Harbor Collection Museum
Northeast Harbor, ME 04662
(207) 276-5262

Location
Northeast Harbor lies ten miles southwest of Bar Harbor on Mount Desert Island.

Highlights
History of Maine coastal life

General Information
The Great Harbor Collection, founded in 1982, is the result of the work and generosity of local townspeople. Virtually all of the exhibit items are on loan to the collection and depict almost all facets of Maine coastal life—fishing and lobstering, domestic life, many trades and professions, and a host of other objects and photographs celebrating "the way things used to be."

Special exhibits of maritime interest include models of the steamboats *Rangeley* and *J. T. Morse* as well as "Life at Mt. Desert Rock Lighthouse," a series of glass-plate photographs taken at the light in 1907.

Activities
Various heritage activities depicting the area's culture

Admission
Open Monday–Saturday, 10 A.M.–5 P.M., the end of June–September.

PEMAQUID POINT
Fishermen's Museum and Pemaquid Point Lighthouse

Fishermen's Museum and Pemaquid
Point Lighthouse
Lighthouse Park
Pemaquid Point, ME 04554
(207) 677-2494/2726

Location
Pemaquid Point Lighthouse is located sixty miles northeast of Portland.

Highlights
Wall-size chart of all the coastal lighthouses in Maine
Fresnel lighthouse lens built in France
Working half-models of fish boats and a whaler

General Information
The Pemaquid Point Lighthouse was commissioned by John Quincy Adams in 1827. Its 1,000-candlepower beam is visible from up to fourteen miles at sea. The town of Bristol owns and maintains the surrounding park and the Fishermen's Museum, now housed in the old lightkeeper's dwelling. The light, though not attended, is a familiar navigational aid to fishermen and all coastal traffic. It is a working light and thus is not open to the public.

Displays at the Fishermen's Museum include charts of lighthouses along the coast of Maine which are numbered to correspond to a wall-size navigational chart; a bronze buoy bell with iron chain; and a Lyle gun for shooting a lifeline to ships in distress. Also presented are tools used in lobstering and gear for several different methods of harvesting sea creatures. A lens identical to the one in the tower of the lighthouse is featured.

The museum exhibits are located in four galleries: the Navigation Room, with navigation displays; the Fish House, with workbenches, tools, and gear used in the lobstering and fishing industries; the Net Room, where several different methods of harvesting fish are displayed, including a small scallop dredge and a sink-gill net used to catch cod and haddock; and the Gallery, where working half-models of fish boats as well as models of a whaler are displayed. A photographic record of the building of a schooner, scrapbooks containing information on fishing, shrimping, and shipwrecks, as well as albums of old postcards, documents, and newspaper articles pertaining to the area, are of special interest.

Admission
No entry fee, but donations accepted. Open Monday–Saturday, 10 A.M.–5 P.M., Sunday, 11 A.M.–5 P.M., Memorial Day–Columbus Day. Other times by appointment.

PORTLAND
Cumberland and Oxford Canal Association

Cumberland and Oxford
Canal Association
36 Lester Drive
Portland, ME 04103
(207) 797-2745

c/o History Department
University of Southern Maine
96 Falmouth Street
Portland, ME 04103
(207) 780-4284

Location
From Portland, take I-95 to SR-26/302 to Bridgton. Then take SR-117 to Harrison.

Highlights
Canal history

General Information
Founded in 1972, the Cumberland and Oxford Canal Association was established to preserve the Cumberland and Oxford Canal as

it was from 1830 to 1872. The canal had its origin in 1791 but was not completed until 1831. From its celebrated opening on 1 June 1830 to its official closing in 1872, it saw heavy traffic, with the height in the 1830s, when as many as 150 boats were registered to operate along the three-day route from Harrison to Portland, Maine.

Artifacts of the canal may be found in the following: the museum at Gorham Campus of the University of Maine; the Parson Smith House in Windham; the residence of Ralph Willis, Little Falls, Gorham; and the Maine Historical Society Library in Portland, where books and records of the canal may also be found.

Admission
No entry fee. Visit the canal in many locations, from Harrison and Bridgton to Naples, Windham, and Portland.

Lightship Nantucket

Lightship Nantucket
465 Congress Street, Suite M
Portland, ME 04101
(207) 775-1181

Location
The *Nantucket*'s home port is Portland, Maine.

Highlights
The *Nantucket* (lightship)
The *Welcome Aboard* (newsletter)

General Information
The Nantucket Lightship Station, first occupied on 15 June 1854, was considered the most remote and dangerous lightship location in the world. It marked the southern limits of the dangerous Nantucket Shoals and the eastern end of the Ambrose shipping channel to New York. Due to the vast amount of traffic passing through the area, it has often been referred to as "the Times Square of the North Atlantic."

At one time some seventy lightships were stationed along our coasts. Today, none remains. The *Nantucket*'s station was the last to be automated (1983). All lightships in the United States have been retired or replaced by Large Navigational Buoys or Texas Towers. The lightship is passing into history just as the coasting schooner and the whaleship have.

In 1975 the lightship *Nantucket* was decommissioned, taken to Nantucket Island, and leased by the town to the Nantucket Historical Association for use as a maritime museum. In 1984 Nantucket Lightship Preservation, Inc., acquired the vessel from the town and continued her operation as a museum on the island until September 1985, when she was towed to Boston for the beginning of extensive restoration work.

Subsequently, the lightship *Nantucket* was sold to Lightship Nantucket, Inc., which now operates the lightship as a maritime museum "to educate the general public and to promote and increase the general public's awareness of the maritime history of the United States . . . and the history of the Nantucket Lightship." Presently wintering in Portland, Maine, the ship is open for public display and educational programs on the East Coast.

Admission

Call or write the museum for information about their opening hours.

ROCKLAND
Owl's Head Light

Officer in Charge
Owl's Head Light
Rockland, ME 04844
(207) 594-8960

Location

The light is situated five miles southeast of Rockland (eighty-one miles northeast of Portland) off SR-73.

Highlights

Lighthouse

General Information
Owl's Head Light (1826) stands on a tree-studded promontory that juts into the Penobscot Bay, affording outstanding views. The headland shape gave rise to the name Owl's Head, which is readily identified by the two hollows in the rocky cliff and ridge between them that form the owl's eyes and beak. A granite breakwater, extending seven-eighths of a mile across Penobscot Bay, leads to Rockland's lighthouse. The town's historic Main Street district is now a shopping area.

Owl's Head Light saw eleven wrecks between 1873 and 1896. In the 1930s it was the home of a dog named Spot, who saved the Matinicus Island mail boat by barking into the raging gale. When Captain Ames heard the dog, he regained his bearings and powered into Rockland safely.

Admission
Grounds: open year-round.

Tower: open to groups by appointment.

Shore Village Museum

Shore Village Museum
104 Limerock Street
P.O. Box 546
Rockland, ME 04841-0546
(207) 594-4950 or 236-3206

Location
From Portland, follow I-95 twenty-three miles north to Rte. 1. Head east for fifty-five miles into Rockland.

Highlights
Civil War records
Lighthouse lenses
Ship models
Scrimshaw
Shore Village Museum (newsletter)

General Information
Shore Village Museum, founded in 1977, contains collections of Civil War records, weapons, and uniforms; lighthouse artifacts; John W. Flint collection of nautical instruments and marine artifacts; related books; and marine items from the U.S. Coast Guard, including working foghorns and lights. Also exhibited are thirty-four dolls dressed in historic costumes, scrimshaw, lobstering tools, ship models, items of local historic interest, and the largest collection of lighthouse lenses and artifacts on display in America. A "please touch" museum invites children to come and enjoy.

Activities
Guided tours, lectures, gallery talks, and special programs

Admission
No entry fee. Open daily, 10 A.M.–4 P.M., June–15 October. Other times by appointment.

ROCKPORT
The Rockport Apprentice Shop

The Rockport Apprentice Shop
P.O. Box 539
Sea Street
Rockport, ME 04856
(207) 236-6071

Location
Take I-95 north from Portland twenty-three miles to Brunswick. Exit onto Rte. 1, heading east by northeast the sixty miles into Rockport (just north of Rockland). The shop is located on Pascall Avenue at Rockport Harbor.

Highlights
Traditional wooden boatbuilding

General Information
The Rockport Apprentice Shop is a delightful program that delves into the past by teaching how to build wooden boats. Apprentices,

under the guidance of a master builder, construct traditional plank-on-frame small craft ranging in size from eight-foot prams to thirty-five-foot schooners. Importantly, the act of boatbuilding itself is not enough. Recording the shape, function, technologies, and derivation of the boats and methods of the past and the present, both national and international, is a caring obligation practiced here.

From the Visitor's Gallery you can study hands-on boatbuilding in progress on the main floor below. Exhibits include boats, models, photographs, and marine art, all celebrating and interpreting our maritime heritage in small craft.

Activities
Two-year program to learn boatbuilding skills, six-week volunteer program, and six-week boatbuilding course

Admission
No entry fee. Open daily, 10 A.M.–5 P.M., year-round.

SEARSPORT
Penobscot Marine Museum

Penobscot Marine Museum
Church Street
P.O. Box 403
Searsport, ME 04974
(207) 548-2529/6634

Location
Searsport is equidistant between Bangor (to the north) and Camden (to the south) on the upper Penobscot Bay. The museum sits at the corner of Rte. 1 and Church Street.

Highlights
Ship models
Finest collection of marine paintings in Maine
The Bay Chronicle (newsletter)
Library (4,000 volumes)

General Information

Penobscot Marine Museum, founded in 1936, is a cluster of seven buildings, including a captain's home (1860), the old town hall (1845), and two houses dating from 1825 and 1880. It contains collections of paintings, ship models, navigational instruments, builders' half-models, shipbuilders' tools, boats, and American and Oriental furnishings. Marine paintings by Thomas and James Buttersworth are also on display.

The new permanent exhibit, "Challenge of the Down-Easters," depicts the Penobscot Bay area's operation of these square-rigged ships.

The library on maritime history is available for use on the premises by appointment.

Activities

Guided tours

Admission

Entry fee. Open Monday–Saturday, 9:30 A.M.–5 P.M., Sunday, 1 P.M.–5 P.M., Memorial Day weekend–15 October.

SOUTH PORTLAND

Spring Point Museum

Spring Point Museum
Southern Maine Vocational
Technical Institute
Fort Road
South Portland, ME 04106
(207) 799-6337

Location

At Portland, take I-295 to SR-77 south to South Portland. The museum is located on the waterfront at Fort Preble on the campus of Southern Maine Vocational Technical Institute.

Highlights

The *Snow Squall* (clipper)
Spring Point Lighthouse and walkway
Fort Preble

General Information
The Spring Point Museum was founded in 1986 to provide for the collection, preservation, display, and interpretation to the public of memorabilia, artifacts, records, and other information of historical significance to South Portland and the surrounding area. Special exhibits are mounted periodically. The museum also features the thirty-five-foot bow section of the extreme clipper ship *Snow Squall*. Built at South Portland in 1851, the 742-ton vessel sailed for thirteen years out of New York to San Francisco and the Far East. In 1864 she put into Port Stanley, Falkland Islands, and was condemned after sustaining severe damage trying to round Cape Horn. She lay there for almost a century and a quarter.

The *Snow Squall* Project accomplished the recovery of about thirty-five feet of her bow for display at the Spring Point Museum as the only remaining example of an American-built clipper and as a memorial to Maine's role in the greatest age of sail and the American merchant marine. Preservation of the ship's timbers and artifacts is a continuing activity of the museum.

Activities
Guided tours are given during regular opening hours and by appointment.

Admission
Open Wednesday–Sunday, 1 P.M.–4 P.M., year-round. Other times by appointment.

YARMOUTH
Museum of Yarmouth History

Museum of Yarmouth History
Main Street
P.O. Box 107
Yarmouth, ME 04096
(207) 846-6259

Location
Take exit 16 on I-295 to Rte. 1. Exit onto Rte. 115, the main street in Yarmouth. (Yarmouth is just nine miles north of Portland on Casco Bay.) Merrill Memorial Library houses the museum.

Highlights
History of Yarmouth and North Yarmouth

General Information
The Museum of Yarmouth History focuses on both Yarmouth and North Yarmouth, a coastal community settled in 1636. Yarmouth history has always been linked to the sea, especially in the nineteenth century when it was home to many shipyards and sea captains.

Museum exhibits include photographs, shipbuilding tools, instruments, and ship paintings. Research materials include journals and documents.

Admission
Donations welcome. Open Monday–Friday, 10 A.M.–4 P.M., July and August; Tuesday–Saturday, 10 A.M.–4 P.M., September–June.

YORK

John Hancock Warehouse and Wharf/ Old York Historical Society

John Hancock Warehouse and Wharf/
Old York Historical Society
P.O. Box 312
York, ME 03909
(207) 363-4974

Location
Exit off I-95 onto SR-91 in the southwest corner of Maine. The wharf and warehouse are on Lindsay Road and the bank of the York River.

Highlights
The *Captain Edward H. Adams* (open-decked barge)
Library
Gift shop

General Information

John Hancock Warehouse and Wharf were built in the eighteenth century and established as a museum and historical site in 1984. It documents three hundred years of commercial life along the York River. Of the many wharves and warehouses that fronted the river and York Harbor (then Lower Town) in the eighteenth century, the John Hancock Warehouse is the only remaining commercial building from the colonial period in York. A reproduced nineteenth-century "gundalow" (an open-decked barge with a sixty-nine foot lateen sail used since the mid-1600s as a river freighter), the *Captain Edward H. Adams* is usually tied up at the wharf when it is not on tour.

Guides will lead you through six museum buildings that date from 1740 to 1940 and portray community, commercial, maritime, and family life from those periods. Collections include furnishings and other maritime artifacts from wealthy shipowners and merchants.

Activities

Guided tours, library for research, decorative arts, genealogy, early manuscripts, documents pertaining to York County, and some maritime materials.

Admission

Entry fee. Open Tuesday–Saturday, 10 A.M.–4 P.M., mid-June–30 September.

NEW HAMPSHIRE

PORTSMOUTH
Port of Portsmouth Maritime Museum

USS *Albacore*
Portsmouth Maritime Museum
P.O. Box 4367
Portsmouth, NH 03801
(603) 436-3680

Location
Travel sixty-five miles north of Boston on I-95. The museum is at Albacore Park in Portsmouth, one-quarter mile from exit 7 on Market Street.

Highlights
The USS *Albacore* (AGSS-569) (submarine)

General Information
The Port of Portsmouth Maritime Museum, established October 1985, features the USS *Albacore* (AGSS-569: research submarine). Built at the Portsmouth Naval Shipyard and launched in 1953, the *Albacore* served with the U.S. Navy from 1953 to 1972 though it never fired a weapon, and never went to war. Primarily, the submarine was used for testing dive brakes, sonar systems, escape mechanisms, and all manner of innovative theories. The *Albacore* was a laboratory afloat. Its teardrop hull design is a triumph and a model for contemporary submarines the world over.

Activities
Tours of the *Albacore* and a documentary

Admission
Entry fee. Open daily, 9:30 A.M.–5:30 P.M., year-round.

The Gloucester fishermen were proud of their ability to fish and race. Here, the *Henry Ford* is moving swiftly through the water in the Gloucester Races on 31 August 1923. (All rights reserved; Rosenfeld Collections, Mystic Seaport Museum, Inc.)

VERMONT

SHELBURNE
Shelburne Museum, Inc.

Shelburne Museum, Inc.
Route 7
Shelburne, VT 05482
(802) 985-3344 (tape recording); 985-3346

Location
Shelburne lies seven miles south of Burlington on Rte. 7.

Highlights
Thirty-seven historic buildings on forty-five parklike acres
The SS *Ticonderoga* (paddle wheeler)
Colchester Reef Lighthouse
Covered Bridge
Scrimshaw
Newsletter
Research library

General Information
Shelburne Museum, Inc., founded in 1947, exhibits a collection of American fine, folk, decorative, and utilitarian art; regional architecture; the SS *Ticonderoga,* the last vertical-beam passenger and freight sidewheel steamer intact in the United States; steam train and private car; carriages and horse-drawn vehicles; toys and dolls; tools; weapons and hunting trophies; American Indian artifacts; Old Master and Impressionist paintings, drawings, and sculptures; and a horticultural and arboreal collection.

Also exhibited is Colchester Reef Lighthouse (1871) from Lake Champlain, which contains maritime prints, figureheads, scrimshaw, early maps, and charts. The covered bridge (c. 1845) is the only double-lane covered bridge with a footpath in Vermont. Horse-drawn vehicles carry visitors around the grounds.

The museum is an assembly of everything that is distinctively characteristic of New England. Each structure is unique, including the 220-foot steam paddle wheeler SS *Ticonderoga,* hauled from nearby Lake Champlain to its final "port," the Shelburne Museum. A research library is also available on the premises.

Activities
Lectures, tours, and research library

Admission
Entry fee (second consecutive day free). Memberships are available. Open daily, 9 A.M.–5 P.M., mid-May–mid-October; Sunday, 11 A.M.–4 P.M., late October–mid-May.

NEW YORK (UPPER)

AMSTERDAM
Fort Hunter

Schoharie Crossing State Historic Site
P.O. Box 140
Fort Hunter, NY 12069
(518) 829-7516

Location
Amsterdam is thirty-four miles northwest of Albany at exit 27 (Rtes. 5 and 58) off the New York State Thruway.

Highlights
Erie Canal locks
Schoharie aqueduct
Restored canal store building (c. 1850)

General Information
At Schoharie Crossing State Historic Site, visitors can view the remains of the Erie Canal, the most dramatic engineering achievement of its time. In addition to the original canal (1825), the enlarged canal (1840s), and the barge canal (1917), one can see many of the engineering structures that contributed to the canal's success. These include the Schoharie aqueduct, several canal locks, culverts, and a canal basin.

The site also encompasses a Visitor's Center, Putman's Store (a restored canal store dating from the 1850s), and a two-and-a-half-mile nature and bike trail along the canal's towpath.

Admission
No entry fee for tours and rides. Grounds are open dawn to dusk year-round.

Museum hours: Open Wednesday–Saturday, 10 A.M.–5 P.M., Sunday, 1 P.M.–5 P.M., 1 May–31 October.

Wagon rides: Open Saturdays, 11 A.M.–3 P.M., 1 July–Labor Day.

Walking tours: Open Wednesday–Friday, 11 A.M.–2 P.M., May–October.

Special groups may reserve in advance.

BLUE MOUNTAIN LAKE
Adirondack Museum

Adirondack Museum
The Adirondack Historical Association
Attn: Maritime Section
P.O. Box 99
Blue Mountain Lake, NY 12812
(518) 352-7311

Location
Blue Mountain Lake is 103 miles north of Albany (44 miles west of I-87) near the junction of Rtes. 28 and 30.

Highlights
Collection of nonpowered freshwater craft
Gift shop

General Information
Adirondack Museum, founded in 1957, is a regional museum of history and art whose specialties include its maritime collections.

A 12,000-square-foot exhibit on boats and boating in the region includes over 60 craft on display from the museum's collection of 203. Some of these are the ten-pound Rushton one-man canoe, the *Sairy Gamp,* Rushton sailing canoes, 60 Adirondack guideboats, and an *Idem*-class sailboat circa 1900. Power craft include the Gold Cup racers *El Lagarto* (1934–36) and *Skeeter* (1905). Still other exhibits include small boats, canoes, rowboats, and the Adirondack guideboat (circa 1800).

Activities
Workshops, canoe building, and guideboat building

Admission
No entry fee. Open daily, 9:30 A.M.–5:30 P.M., Memorial Day–mid-October.

CANASTOTA
Canastota Canal Town Museum

Canastota Canal Town Museum
122 Canal Street
Canastota, NY 13032
(315) 697-3451

Location
Canastota is forty-eight miles east of Syracuse off I-90.

Highlights
Erie Canal history

General Information
Canastota Canal Town Museum, founded in 1970, was established to preserve the Erie Canal's heritage. Construction of the Erie Canal was hailed as the greatest engineering accomplishment up to that time. Under the leadership of DeWitt Clinton, construction began in 1817 and was completed in 1825. The canal connected

Albany, on the east, to Buffalo, on the west, and it became the main route between the Atlantic Ocean and the Great Lakes.

The 1860 canal-era museum building is filled with authentic memorabilia as well as exhibits of local businesses.

Admission
Entry fee. Open Monday–Friday, 10 A.M.–4 P.M., year-round. Other times by appointment.

CLAYTON
Thousand Islands Shipyard Museum

Thousand Islands Shipyard Museum
750 Mary Street
Clayton, NY 13624
(315) 686-4104

Location
Take I-81 north from Syracuse the ninety-four miles to Fisher's Landing, then bear west on SR-12 the five miles to Clayton. The museum is five miles south of the Thousand Islands Bridge on SR-12N.

Highlights
The *Dixie II* and *Miss Canada III* (Gold Cup racers)
The River Memories Museum and Store
Wooden boat collection
Library (500 volumes)

General Information
Thousand Islands Shipyard Museum, initially founded in 1964 and more formally organized in 1980, is housed in a mid-1800 stone building and six other buildings. The museum was the outgrowth of the Antique Boat Auxiliary, which was formed as a component of Clayton's Old Town Hall Museum.

The museum is a treasure of freshwater boating history, housing a collection of wooden boats that includes native American dugout and birchbark canoes, St. Lawrence skiffs, early twentieth-century speedboats, launches, dispros (a small fishing boat with a disappearing propeller, hence the nickname—dispro), skiffputts, sailing craft, rowing craft, and pleasure boats. Collections also include duckboats, outboards, outboard and inboard engines, runabouts, ice boats, a photography collection, and tools.

Featured are: the *Dixie II,* winner of the 1908–10 Gold Cup powerboat races; the *Miss Canada III* and other Gold Cup boats; and personal boats used by Presidents Grant and Garfield, as well as other historic craft. Also featured is the *Pardon Me,* one of the largest and most elegant runabouts ever built, and George Boldt's runabout, the *PDQ*.

Activities
Guided tours, lectures, study clubs, hobby workshops, charters, and cruises. Small-craft boatbuilding school during the summer. Antique boat tour rides daily from the museum grounds. The museum also hosts a large antique boat show the first weekend in August each year, with over 125 boats on display.

Admission
Entry fee. Open daily, 10 A.M.–4 P.M., mid-May–mid-October.

CROWN POINT

Crown Point State Historic Site/ Crown Point Reservation Campsite

Crown Point State Historic Site
RD #1, Box 219
Crown Point, NY 12928
(518) 597-3666

Location
To reach Crown Point take I-87 north for seventy-three miles from Albany to Chestertown. Exit onto SR-8 toward Hague (twenty-eight miles) to SR-9. Follow it north the fifteen miles to Crown Point (located midway between Albany and Montreal at the southern end of Lake Champlain).

Highlights
Rodin's "La France"
Preserved ruins of the French Fort St. Frédéric (1734–59)
British Fort Crown Point (1759–73)
Champlain Lighthouse
Museum campsite

General Information
Crown Point State Historic Site contains maritime exhibits and is near the Champlain Memorial Lighthouse, which was erected by Vermont and New York in 1909 to honor Samuel de Champlain, who discovered the lake in 1609. The site was a staging area for Colonial armies and the Lake Champlain fleets during the French and Indian and the revolutionary wars.

Lake Champlain was a vital highway linking two diverse regions of British North America. Located midway between Albany and Montreal, it became the center of communication between New York and Canada. The eighteenth-century structures of His Majesty's Fort of Crown Point and the French Fort St. Frédéric are preserved. The modern Visitor's Center exhibits French, British, and American chapters of Crown Point's history.

The light station, a fifty-five-foot limestone tower with keeper's house, was constructed in 1858 and put into operation in 1859 with a 5th-order Fresnel lens. It ceased operation in 1926.

Also exhibited is the bas-relief "La France" by Auguste Rodin, which was a gift from France.

Admission
No entry fee. Open Wednesday–Saturday, 10 A.M.–5 P.M., Sunday, 1 P.M.–5 P.M., May–October. Also open Memorial Day, Fourth of July, and Labor Day. Groups must make reservations in advance.

MAYVILLE

Chautauqua Lakes Historic Vessels Co.

Chautauqua Lake Historic Vessels Co.
15 Water Street
Mayville, NY 14757
(716) 753-7823

Location
Mayville is in the southwest corner of upper state New York, five miles east of Lake Erie off SR-394 between I-90 and SR-17 on the northern end of the Chautauqua Lake waterfront.

Highlights
Chautauqua Belle (sternwheeler)
Sea Lion (sixteenth-century merchant ship)
Bemus Point-Stow Ferry (cable drawn)

General Information
Chautauqua Lake Historic Vessels Co. owns and operates historic vessels, carrying passengers exactly as was done in the past. Once a secret strategic water link between French Canada, the Mississippi River, and French Louisiana, Chautauqua Lake has witnessed a wide variety of vessels in its recorded history.

The Chautauqua Lake historic vessels include: (1) *Chautauqua Belle,* an old-fashioned, steam-powered sternwheeler that pays homage to that magnificent fleet of steamboats that carried cargo and passengers to summer resorts a century ago. With a soft puff of steam and a gentle splash of her paddle wheel, she quietly glides across this scenic inland lake. (2) *Sea Lion,* a sixty-three-foot square-rigged sixteenth-century merchant ship that gives passengers the unique experience of life under sail 400 years ago. (3) Bemus Point-Stow Ferry, perhaps the last of a truly American pioneer transport. This cable-drawn ferry has been in operation for over 177 years at the place where one can cross the "Narrows" of Chautauqua Lake either by car or on foot.

Activities
The *Chautauqua Belle*—1-1/2 hour cruises in the summer; The *Sea Lion*—Public sailings one Saturday a month; open for tours Tuesday–Sunday, noon–4:30 P.M.; Bemus Point-Stow Ferry—Ferry rides Saturdays and Sundays only in June, every day in July and August, 11 A.M.–10 P.M.

Admission
Entry fee

WHITEHALL
Skenesborough Museum

Skenesborough Museum
Whitehall, NY 12887
(518) 499-0716

Location
Take I-87 north from Albany the fifty-four miles to Glens Falls. Exit east onto SR-149, traveling the twenty-three miles northeast to Whitehall. The museum is on Skenesborough Drive.

Highlights
Ship models
Gift shop

General Information
Skenesborough Museum, founded in 1959, is located in a building constructed by the New York State Canal System in 1917. The museum's themes—Whitehall navy, lake, canal, railroad—are followed in pictures, artifacts, or models of the Revolution, the War of 1812, and the lake boat period (1811–73).

In 1775 the ship that became the first vessel of the U.S. Navy was captured from the Skene estate on a Green Mountain Boys' foray. Two days later Benedict Arnold's men sailed it to Crown Point where he armed it for a definite act of war—the capture of the British naval ship *Enterprise*.

Boaters may tie up along the canal wall while visiting the museum, and nearby is Lock 12 of the New York Canal System.

Admission
No entry fee, but donations accepted. Open Monday–Saturday, 10 A.M.–5 P.M., Sunday, noon–5 P.M., Memorial Day–12 October.

MASSACHUSETTS

BEVERLY
Beverly Historical Society and Museum

Beverly Historical Society and Museum
117 Cabot Street
Beverly, MA 01915
(617) 922-1186

Location
Beverly (established in 1693) is on SR-1A, twenty-five miles northeast of Boston.

Highlights
Library (3,000 volumes)

General Information
Beverly Historical Society and Museum, founded in 1891, includes general maritime history through a 3,000-volume library that includes extensive shipping papers and logbooks. (Of historical note, on 5 September 1775 at Glovers Wharf in Beverly, George Washington commissioned the schooner *Hannah*.)

Admission
Entry fee. Memberships are available. Open Wednesday–Saturday, 10 A.M.–4 P.M., Sunday, 1 P.M.–4 P.M., 20 May–15 October; Thursday–Saturday, 10 A.M.–4 P.M., 16 October–19 May. Memorial Day and Columbus Day, 1 P.M.–4 P.M.

BOSTON
Boston Marine Society

Boston Marine Society
National Historical Park
Building 32, Charlestown Navy Yard
Boston, MA 02129
(617) 242-0522

Location
In Boston take I-93 to Rte. 1 north. Follow signs to the Charlestown Navy Yard across Charlestown Bridge.

Highlights
Oil paintings
Ship models

General Information
Boston Marine Society, founded in 1742, maintains a collection of artifacts, oil paintings, and ship models.

Admission
No entry fee. Open Monday–Friday, 10 A.M.–3 P.M., year-round.

Boston Tea Party Ship and Museum

The Boston Tea Party Ship and Museum
Congress Street Bridge on Harbor Walk
Boston, MA 02210
(617) 338-1773

Location
The museum is located at the Congress Street Bridge on Harbor Walk, the south side of Boston's downtown area.

Highlights
The *Beaver II* (brig)
Tea Times (newsletter)
Gift shop

General Information
On the night of 16 December 1773, a small band of Bostonians climbed aboard three vessels moored at Griffin's Wharf and destroyed 340 chests of dutied tea by dumping them into the harbor. ("Rally Mohawks/Bring out your axes!/And tell King George/We'll pay no taxes!") This violent protest to Parliament's tax on tea—the Boston Tea Party—shattered a three-year period of relative calm between Great Britain and her colonies. It led, almost

without interruption, to the outbreak of war at Lexington and Concord.

The Boston Tea Party Ship and Museum dramatically re-creates the notorious 1773 protest in the museum exhibits and aboard the full-scale working replica of one of the original tea party ships, the brig *Beaver II*. This 110-foot brigantine sailed across the Atlantic with a cargo of tea and is now moored at the Tea Party site. (When your tour ends you will be in the Protest Room. "Take a stand" and voice or write your protest. Everyone does!)

Activities
Activities include viewing an audiovisual presentation on the ship's voyage and the taxing of the tea, tossing tea chests overboard, and talking with colonial guides. Complimentary tea is served.

Admission
Entry fee. Open daily, 9 A.M.–dusk, year-round.

Charlestown Navy Yard
(*See also:* USS *Constitution*)

Charlestown Navy Yard
Attn: Superintendent
Boston NHP
15 State Street
Boston, MA 02109
(617) 241-9078

Location
Follow signs along I-93 to Rte. 1, then turn immediately off onto Constitution Road to the yard just north of downtown Boston.

Highlights
The *Constitution* ("Old Ironsides" herself)
The *Cassin Young* (1943 destroyer)

General Information
The "Yard" has one of the oldest drydocks in the country and a historic ropewalk which exists side-by-side with forge shops, a marine railway, and officers' quarters. "Old Ironsides," the oldest fully commissioned warship in the world, was the first ship to use the drydock.

Activities
Self-guided and guided tours

Admission
Entry fee. Open daily, 9:30 A.M.–5:30 P.M., year-round. Public docking is available at Pier 4 and nearby marinas.

USS *Constitution*

(*See also:* Charlestown Navy Yard)

USS *Constitution*
Charlestown Navy Yard
Charlestown, MA 02129
(617) 242-5670

Location
Across the wharf from the USS *Constitution* Museum, the USS *Constitution* is docked at the Charlestown Navy Yard. Follow signs along I-93 to Rte. 1, then turn immediately off onto Constitution Road to the yard, just north of downtown Boston.

Highlights
The USS *Constitution* ("Old Ironsides")

General Information
The USS *Constitution* was launched in 1797 and has been in restoration ever since. It is a forty-four-gun frigate that served this country well. In 1794, when the *Constitution* and five other frigates were authorized, the new United States of America had been without a navy for nine years. Because of Barbary (North African) pirates, merchants who traded in the Mediterranean found it increasingly more difficult to conduct business. And there was no

U.S. Navy to stop them. Thus, the *Constitution* was built by Joshua Humphreys and Josia Fox to be powerful enough to defeat any enemy of equal size and fast enough to outsail a stronger opponent.

Activities
The Visitor Center will direct you to the self-guided tours.

Admission
No entry fee. Open daily and holidays, 9:30 A.M.–3:30 P.M., year-round.

USS *Constitution* Museum

USS *Constitution* Museum
Boston National Historical Park
Charlestown Navy Yard
P.O. Box 1812
Boston, MA 02129
(617) 242-0543

Location
Across the wharf from the USS *Constitution* at the Charlestown Navy Yard in Boston is the USS *Constitution* Museum.

Highlights
Computer and hands-on exhibits
Video presentation
Constitution Chronicle (newsletter)
Research library

General Information
The USS *Constitution* Museum, founded in 1972, houses objects related to life aboard ship, objects removed during restorations of the *Constitution,* examples of sailors' arts, historic memorabilia, and decorative arts related to the *Constitution* and the early sailing Navy. Hands-on exhibits examine the construction of "Old Ironsides," her history and preservation, and the lives of her sailors. Replicas of such components as her keel, yardarms, and sick bay evoke a sense of the complexity of the ship's design.

On 21 October 1797, the USS *Constitution* slid down the ways just three years after the laying of her keel. She is the oldest commissioned ship in the U.S. Navy. Shown here shadowing Boston's modern architecture, the *Constitution* makes her once-a-year turn in Boston Harbor. (Photo courtesy of the USS *Constitution* Museum.)

Visitors of all ages can climb the fighting top, touch the full-size cross section of the hull, raise a sail, swing in the hammocks, and steer the ship's wheel on a rolling deck. A fifteen-minute video based on the actual journals of the *Constitution*'s surgeon chronicles the challenges he faced during the battle with HMS *Java* in the War of 1812.

Visitors can also step into the shoes of captain, lieutenant, able-bodied seaman, marine, or nine-year-old "Powder Monkey" by playing at the computer exhibit. See what kind of decisions you would make during "The Great Chase," when the *Constitution* escaped from five British frigates during her first encounter with the British in the War of 1812.

The library, access to which is available by appointment only, contains research materials related to naval and maritime history, originals and microfilm copies of ship logs, personal journals and letters, and plans of "Old Ironsides."

Activities
Special programs for school groups by reservation, audiovisual programs, gun drills and performances by the Volunteer Marine Corps Detachment of 1797, and maritime artisan workshops and demonstrations are scheduled periodically.

Admission
Entry fee. Children under six are admitted free. Memberships are available. Open daily, 9 A.M.–6 P.M. in summer; 10 A.M.–4 P.M. in winter; and 9 A.M.–5 P.M. in spring and fall. Closed Thanksgiving, Christmas, and New Year's Day. The museum is wheelchair accessible.

Museum of Science

Museum of Science
Science Park
Boston, MA 02114
(617) 723-2500

Location
The museum is located at the Charles River Dam, McGrath and O'Brien Circle in Cambridge, adjacent to downtown Boston.

Highlights
Ship models

General Information
The Museum of Science contains novel nautical displays. The first floor contains a full-size replica of a ship's bridge. Visitors can visualize steering their vessel through dangerous waters while standing at the big wheel. Nearby is a large diorama of East Boston's McKay Shipyard where the famed *Flying Cloud* clipper ship was built. Ship models ranging from ancient Egyptian sailing

craft to modern power vessels are found on the museum's second floor. Through the window you'll glimpse three typical harbor buoys once having served at sea. They are now floating in the Charles River basin. A plaque describes their original uses.

Admission
Entry fee. Open Tuesday–Thursday, Saturday and Sunday, 9 A.M.–5 P.M., Friday, 9 A.M.–9 P.M., year-round.

The Old State House—The Bostonian Society

The Old State House
206 Washington Street
Boston, MA 02109
(617) 720-1713

Location
On the Freedom Trail in downtown Boston, the Old State House sits at 206 Washington Street (at State Street).

Highlights
Ship models
Marine paintings
Maritime wood sculpture
Scrimshaw
Extensive research library (6,000 volumes)
Gift shop

General Information
The Old State House, built in 1713, was the site of many events leading to the American Revolution, such as James Otis's speech protesting the Writs of Assistance, the Stamp Act Debates, and the Boston Massacre.

From its balcony, the Declaration of Independence was first read to Bostonians in 1776. The building contains a museum maintained by the Bostonian Society, which was founded in 1881 to rescue the Old State House from demolition. The museum's exhibits, including a fine collection of maritime artifacts, illustrate the history of the city of Boston. Among these are: a selection of nineteenth-century ship models representing Boston vessels; seascapes, ship portraits, and views of Boston Harbor; a life-size female figurehead carved by Isaac Fowle; navigational instruments; and scrimshaw.

The noncirculating library contains over 6,000 books, maps, documents, and broadsides related to Boston history. A reading area is available for researchers. The museum's gift shop sells guidebooks, books on Boston history and marine subjects, reproductions of American colonial and maritime objects, and a wide variety of souvenirs.

Activities
Lectures, gallery talks, and guided tours available by appointment

Admission
Entry fee. Open daily, 9:30 A.M.–5 P.M. in summer; Monday–Friday, 10 A.M.–4 P.M., Saturday, 9:30 A.M.–5 P.M., Sunday, 11 A.M.–5 P.M. in winter. Closed Thanksgiving, Christmas, New Year's Day, and Easter. Library open weekdays, 9:30 A.M.–4:30 P.M.

Note: The Old State House closed for renovations for at least one year in early 1990. Please call ahead for visits in 1990 and 1991.

BUZZARDS BAY
Capt. Charles H. Hurley Library

Capt. Charles H. Hurley Library
Nantucket Way
P.O. Box D
Buzzards Bay, MA 02532
(508) 759-5761

Location
At the beginning of Cape Cod, Buzzards Bay is sixty miles southeast of Boston off I-495. Exit onto Rte. 6, heading east four miles.

Highlights
Library (36,000 volumes on transportation and engineering)

General Information
Capt. Charles H. Hurley Library, founded in 1980, has collections, archives, and ninety-five scale models set in a base that represents the sea and provides a panoramic background. The library features books primarily on maritime transportation and engineering. They are available for in-house or interlibrary loan. Reading rooms are likewise available.

Activities
Guided tours, lectures, education programs, and library

Admission
No entry fee. Open Monday–Friday, 9 A.M.–5 P.M., September–June. Hours vary when school is not in session.

CAMBRIDGE
Hart Nautical Collections

Hart Nautical Collections
MIT Museum
265 Massachusetts Avenue
Cambridge, MA 02139
(617) 253-5942

Location
Across the Charles River from Boston in Cambridge, these collections are reached by entering the lobby at 77 Massachusetts Avenue, then turning right down the hall heading in the direction of the Charles River.

Highlights
Ship models
Major collections of working drawings

General Information
The Francis Russell Hart Nautical Museum (now the Hart Nautical Collections) was founded at the Massachusetts Institute of Technology (MIT) in Cambridge in 1922. Its purpose is to illustrate the evolution and current trends in naval architecture and ship-

building for the MIT Department of Ocean Engineering and the general public.

The Hart Nautical Collections became a part of the MIT Museum in 1981. The MIT Museum now continues the original commitment of the Hart Nautical Museum by preserving and interpreting the history of one of the oldest engineering fields; namely, ship design and construction. Exhibits include exquisitely crafted model ships built to scale, descriptively labeled so you can wander about on your own. Models range from simple—a tiny, plain Norwegian pram—to complex—a four-foot reproduction of the U.S. frigate *President,* fully rigged, complete with coiled lines, lifeboats, and brass fittings.

For exotica, the Korean warship *Turtle* has a spiked cover to shelter its gunners and crew. The sixteenth-century real ship spouted sulfuric fumes from the *Turtle*'s mouth to frighten its superstitious foes and to provide a smoke screen.

Major Collections

Captain Arthur H. Clark Collections—paintings, photographs, prints, plans of vessels, half-models, and books
Allan Forbes Collection—paintings and prints of whales
C. H. W. Foster collection—yachting photographs (1885–1930)
Haffenreffer-Herreshoff Collection—working drawings
McInnis-Lawley Collection—working drawings
Gordon Munro Collection—working drawings and models (1915–1940)
George Owen Collection—working drawings and models (1902–1958)
Frank C. Paine Collection—working drawings, models, and photographs (1923–1939)
Bethlehem Steel Collection—working drawings and photographs (1851–1940)

Admission

No entry fee. For appointments call (617) 253-5942. Research by appointment only at 265 Massachusetts Avenue.

COHASSET
Cohasset Maritime Museum

Cohasset Historical Society
14 Summer Street
Cohasset, MA 02025
(617) 383-6930

Location
Cohasset is a suburb of Boston, fifteen miles to the south. Take Rte. 3A, exiting onto SR-228. Travel one mile to North Main, then head east to Cohasset.

Highlights
Ship models
1760 ship chandlery

General Information
Cohasset Maritime Museum was established in 1957. Its collections relate to the town's seafaring history: shipwreck relics; lifesaving equipment; nineteenth-century maritime artifacts; sailing ship models; paintings; early tools; Indian stone artifacts; and general historical artifact collections of local origin. (Cohasset was settled around 1670 as the eastern part of Hingham. Captain John Smith visited here briefly in 1614 to trade with Quonshasset Indians.)

Activities
Guided tours and summer walking tours of Cohasset

Admission
Entry fee. Memberships are available. Open Tuesday–Sunday, 1:30 P.M.–4:30 P.M., mid-June–late September.

ESSEX
Essex Shipbuilding Museum

Essex Shipbuilding Museum
28 Main Street
Essex, MA 01929
(508) 768-7541

Location
Take SR-28 north from Boston toward Gloucester. At the intersection with Rte. 133, head inland (west) the seven miles to Essex.

Highlights
Hands-on exhibits
Shipbuilding documents
Rigged ship models and half-models
Photographs and videotape of the *Ste. Rosalie*'s (dragger) construction

General Information
Essex Shipbuilding Museum, founded in 1976, occupies an 1835 schoolhouse where many of the shipbuilders studied. More two-masted vessels were built in Essex than in any other town in the world. The fishing fleets of Gloucester and Boston, for example, were built here.

Adjacent is the Old Burying Ground where many shipbuilding family ancestors, Burnhams and Storys, are buried. Just two blocks away is the bank of the Essex River where so many chebacco boats, pinkies, and schooners from the many shipyards in Essex were launched. After the British decimated the fishing fleet, the residents of Chebacco Parrish (now Essex) responded by building hundreds of the small two-man on-shore fishing boats, which became known as chebacco boats, and their slightly larger counterpart, the pinkies.

Activities
The museum maintains an excellent archive of ships' plans, photographs, bills of labor, and other documents of the shipbuilding industry. Model builders, historians, and writers will want to study its contents. The museum welcomes those involved in research, restoration, and relaxation.

Admission
Entry fee (children and Essex residents, excepted). Memberships are available. Open Thursday–Sunday, noon–5 P.M., May–October, other times by appointment.

FALL RIVER
Battleship Cove

Battleship Cove
Central and Water Streets
Fall River, MA 02721
(508) 678-1100

Location
The cove is located underneath the Braga Bridge in Fall River (exit 5 [Rte. 138] off I-195 south from Boston).

Highlights
The USS *John P. Kennedy* (destroyer)
The USS *Lionfish* (submarine)
The USS *Massachusetts* (battleship) (Overnight camping aboard is encouraged)
PT boats 796, 617, and PT Boat Museum and Library
Ship models at nearby Marine Museum at Fall River, Inc.

General Information
Imagine bunking down in the crew's quarters of a 35,000-ton World War II battleship. Eating chow in the ship's wardroom. Exploring the length and breadth of a proud fighting ship that used to be home for more than 2,300 sailors! Visitors can, at Battleship Cove, founded in 1965, where twentieth-century vessels of the U.S. Navy are harbored. Visitors may board the battleship USS *Massachusetts,* the destroyer USS *John P. Kennedy,* the submarine USS *Lionfish,* and PT boats 796 and 617. Or visit the Marine Museum, which includes an exhibit on the *Titanic*.

The collections include equipment and memorabilia connected with the operation of the above ships and a fifty-volume library of naval warfare and the history of the battleship's development as a naval weapon. Flags and ship models are also exhibited.

Admission
Entry fee. Memberships are available. Ships and museum open daily 9 A.M.–6 P.M., July–Labor Day; 9 A.M.–4:30 P.M. the rest of the year. Closed Thanksgiving, Christmas, and New Year's Day.

Marine Museum at Fall River, Inc.

The Marine Museum at Fall River, Inc.
70 Water Street
P.O. Box 1147
Fall River, MA 02722
(508) 674-3533

Location
The museum is housed in an old mill structure just a short walk from the battleship *Massachusetts* at Battleship Cove, Fall River (at the junction of Rte. 138 and I-195).

Highlights
The *Titanic* exhibit
Ship models
Library (2,000 volumes)

General Information
The Marine Museum at Fall River, Inc., was founded in 1968 and acquired its initial collection from the Seaman's Church of New York. Over the years the museum has received other donations and artifacts from United Brands Company (an international shipping firm), Old Colony Railroad, and the Titanic Historical Society.

The famous White Star Line's *Titanic* brings to mind both the triumph and tragedy of the steamship age. Re-created in exact detail by Twentieth Century Fox Studios in 1952 for the movie "Titanic," the one-ton 28-foot-long model is the centerpiece for one of the museum's most popular exhibits.

In 1987 the remains of an eighteenth-century British ship scuttled in Newport Harbor during the Revolutionary War were located. "It's one of the most historic finds in Rhode Island in years," stated the director of the museum. "There's some validity to calling these ships time capsules, as nothing on board has been disturbed since the sinking." Information on these finds is in the museum. Particular attention is paid to the famous Fall River Line (1847–1937), which used Fall River as the New England terminus for its New York to New England run. Memorabilia from the great steamships—"floating palaces"—are included in the museum's exhibits.

Activities
Museum facilities are available for meetings, lectures, etc. The library contains books on maritime history that are available on the premises.

Admission
Entry fee. Memberships are available. Open Monday–Friday, 9 A.M.–4:30 P.M., Saturdays, Sundays, and holidays, 10 A.M.–5 P.M., year-round.

The PT Boat Museum and Library

The PT Boat Museum and Library
Battleship Cove
Fall River, MA 02721
(508) 678-1100
(For Photo Collection and Archives contact:
PT Boats, Inc.
1384 Cordova Road, Suite 2
Germantown, TN 38138)

Location
The museum and library are located at Battleship Cove in Fall River, off I-195 at exit 5.

Highlights
Japanese submarine
Library (1,000 volumes)
Gift shop (mail order for PT boat items)

General Information
The collections at the PT Boat Museum and Library, founded in 1946, include two World War II PT boats, books, diaries, insignias, memorabilia of forty-three operating squadrons of World War II PT boats, tenders and bases, films, photographs, and plans. Also on display is a one-man Japanese suicide submarine.

The library contains books on PT boat operations.

Activities
Nonlending library for serious research, available by appointment. Lectures, films, restoration, and photographic services

Admission
Entry fee. Memberships are available. Open daily, 9 A.M.–5 P.M., year-round.

FALMOUTH
Falmouth Historical Society's Museums

Falmouth Historical Society
P.O. Box 174
Falmouth, MA 02541
(508) 548-4857

Location
From Boston travel south on I-495. Turn onto SR-25 east for five miles to the junction of SR-28. Falmouth is seventeen miles south on SR-28; the museums are on the north side of Village Green at Falmouth Center.

Highlights
Whaling era memorabilia

General Information
Falmouth was settled in 1661 and was a center for whaling and shipbuilding. In the former home of a sea captain, the Falmouth Historical Society's Museums (founded in 1900) maintain a small maritime collection with memorabilia from the whaling era.

Activities
Summer guided tours of a 1790 home (the Julia Wood House), a "museum" building, and a barn with farm equipment.

Admission
Entry fee. Open Monday–Friday, 2 P.M.–5P.M., 15 June–15 September.

GLOUCESTER
Cape Ann Historical Museum

Cape Ann Historical Museum
27 Pleasant Street
Gloucester, MA 01930
(508) 283-0455

Location
The Cape Ann Historical Museum is located in Gloucester (SR-128) at 27 Pleasant Street.

Highlights
Permanent exhibition that explores Cape Ann's fisheries and maritime history
Nation's largest collection of paintings and drawings by marine artist Fitz Hugh Lane (1804–1865)

General Information
The Cape Ann Historical Museum, founded in 1875, features displays of American decorative arts and furnishings and guided tours of the furnished home of Captain Elias Davis, built in 1804 for one of Gloucester's enterprising merchant sea captains.

Activities
Special exhibitions of American artists of the first rank who have worked on Cape Ann, including Marsden Hartley, Frank Duveneck, Walter Hancock, and Milton Avery.

Admission
Entry fee. Open Tuesday–Saturday, 10 A.M.–5 P.M., year-round except February.

Gloucester Fishermen's Museum

Gloucester Fisherman's Museum
Rogers and Porter Streets
Gloucester, MA 01930
(508) 283-1940

Location
Just thirty-eight miles northeast of Boston, Gloucester is off of SR-128 (twenty-three miles east of I-95).

Highlights
Maritime and fishing history

Racing Gloucester fishing vessels was almost as important as the fishing itself. The *Bluenose* was built to race, but she also had to be used in fishing. Thus qualified, she is shown here with the *Henry Ford* (the near ship) in the Gloucester Races on 21 October 1922. (All rights reserved; Rosenfeld Collections, Mystic Seaport Museum, Inc.)

General Information
Gloucester Fishermen's Museum has hands-on exhibits, schooner rooms in its fishing center, movies, and galleries on the world of the sea and fishermen, past and present.

Admission
Open daily, Monday–Saturday, 10 A.M.–4 P.M., Sunday, noon–4 P.M., year-round.

HULL
Hull Lifesaving Museum

Hull Lifesaving Museum
1117 Nantasket Avenue
P.O. Box 221
Hull, MA 02045
(617) 925-5433

Location
By land, take Rte. 3A to Nantasket Beach, or Rte. 3 to Rte. 228 to Nantasket Beach. Follow signs to museum once in Hull. By sea, take Nantasket Ferry from Boston's Long Wharf. When boarding, request stop at Pemberton Pier.

Highlights
Lifeboat

General Information
The Hull Lifesaving Museum is in the Old Point Allerton Lifesaving Station, which was first captained by Joshua James, world-renowned lifesaver.

From the door of the museum one can see for miles out to sea and can photograph Boston Light, the oldest lighthouse in the nation. Nearby, one can look out from Fort Revere's Observation Tower on Telegraph Hill to recognize why this site was chosen to scan Boston Harbor. A walk through Hull village will reveal the buildings Joshua James grew up among, well marked to tell their role during his life.

Visitors can stop at the new Point Allerton Coast Guard Station, still one of the busiest in the country. There today's working fishermen can be seen unloading a catch. Rental boats are available. From there a ferry can be taken to the Harbor Islands or back to Boston.

Activities
Visitors can observe a multimedia program on the life and times of Joshua James, rig a sail boat, learn about using the stars to navigate, sound a foghorn, and even try on a lifesaver's gear.

Admission
No entry fee. Open Wednesday–Sunday, 12 P.M.–5 P.M., July–August; Saturday, Sunday, Monday, and holidays, 12 P.M.–5 P.M., September–June.

LOWELL
Middlesex Canal Museum

Middlesex Canal Museum
University of Lowell
Alumni/Lydon Library
1 University Avenue
Lowell, MA 01854
(508) 452-5000

Location
The museum lies approximately thirty miles north of Boston on the Merrimack River at Lowell.

Highlights
Towpath Topics (quarterly bulletin)

General Information
The Middlesex Canal Museum, founded in 1962 and affiliated with the Middlesex Canal Association, contains archives of that association and its records. The powerful Merrimack River and its canals transformed the community of Lowell from a handicraft center to a textile industrial center.

Admission
No entry fee. Open Monday–Friday, 8:30 A.M.–5 P.M., year-round.

NANTUCKET ISLAND
Nantucket Lifesaving Museum

Nantucket Lifesaving Museum
P.O. Box L, Polpis Road
Nantucket, MA 02554
(508) 228-1885

Location
The museum is located just off Polpis Road only a short distance from Nantucket Center.

Highlights
H. H. Kynett Library and Research Center

General Information
The Nantucket Lifesaving Museum, established in 1972, is housed in an authentic re-creation of the original Surfside Station built by the U.S. Lifesaving Service in 1874.

The museum is dedicated to the drama of human efforts against the relentless sea. The hidden enemy—the death-dealing shoals that surround Nantucket—are still referred to as the "graveyard of the Atlantic." Yesterday and today, those devoted to the saving of lives continue their fight against this adversary and are part of America's maritime history and the Nantucket tradition. The Nantucket Lifesaving Museum proudly honors their valiant endeavor.

The powerful drama of rescue at sea is vividly portrayed at this outstanding museum complex. It contains thrilling accounts through actual photos of daring rescues; original Lifesaving Service boats and rescue equipment; an original Francis Life Car, breeches buoy, and Lyle gun; exciting replicas and original material from the Lighthouse Service and Revenue Cutter Service; quarterboards of vessels wrecked around Nantucket; and architectural plans of original lifesaving stations.

Admission
Open Tuesday–Sunday, 10 A.M.–5 P.M., 15 June–15 October (open to members year-round).

Whaling Museum

Whaling Museum
Broad Street
Nantucket Island, MA 02554
(508) 228-1894

Location
Ferry to Nantucket Island from either Hyannis Port or Woods Hole. The museum is at Broad Street at the head of Steamboat Wharf.

Highlights
A finback whale skeleton (forty-three feet long)
A lighthouse lens (sixteen feet tall)
Scrimshaw
Library

General Information
The Whaling Museum, established in 1846, was built as a factory to refine spermaceti (a waxlike substance taken from the oil in the head of a sperm whale used to make cosmetics, ointments, candles, etc.). The building now houses extensive collections of whaling implements used in the pursuit and processing of sperm whales. The huge press, used to extract the wax from the oil, spans the building where a full-size tryworks, a whaleboat from the bark *Sunbeam,* and an unparalleled collection of scrimshaw are displayed.

The skeleton of a forty-three-foot finback whale is exhibited, and the original sixteen-foot-tall lens from the Sankaty Lighthouse highlights an area devoted to navigation and exploration. Also displayed are paintings and portraits of those who made Nantucket the third largest port in the United States.

The Research Center contains over 5,000 volumes, 315 ships' logs, 500,000 pages of manuscripts, and 10,000 photographs for use by students, historians, and genealogists.

Activities
Guided tours of thirteen historic Nantucket buildings

Admission
Entry fee. Open daily, 10 A.M.–5 P.M., 28 May–12 October; Saturdays and Sundays only, 10 A.M.–5 P.M., 13 October–31 December, and 1 March–27 May. Closed Christmas.

NEW BEDFORD
New Bedford Free Public Library

New Bedford Free Public Library
613 Pleasant Street
New Bedford, MA 02740
(508) 991-6275

Location
New Bedford is seventy miles south of Boston on I-195. The library is located at 613 Pleasant Street in the center of the city.

Highlights
History of whaling
New Bedford Customs House records

General Information
The New Bedford Free Public Library, founded in 1852, contains collections relating to whaling: namely, a index of crews of New Bedford whaling ships that contains 250,000 names; 440 logbooks of whaling ships, 1768–1920; and business records of whaling agents Charles W. Morgan, J. & W. R. Wing, Charles Tucker, and George Hussey.

Admission
No entry fee. Open Monday–Thursday, 9 A.M.–9 P.M., Fridays and Saturdays, 9 A.M.–5 P.M., year-round. Closed national holidays.

New Bedford Whaling Museum

New Bedford Whaling Museum
18 Johnny Cake Hill
New Bedford, MA 02740
(508) 997-0046

Location
This museum is nestled in New Bedford's historic district on Johnny Cake Hill (a road).

Highlights
Half-size (eighty-nine-foot) model of the whaling bark *Lagoda*
Ship models
Scrimshaw
The Bulletin from Johnny Cake Hill (quarterly newsletter)
Library (20,000 volumes)

General Information
Under the sponsorship of the Old Dartmouth Historical Society, the New Bedford Whaling Museum was established in 1907 for the purpose of collecting, exhibiting, interpreting, and preserving the history of American whaling and the local area. The museum is one of the largest in America devoted to local history. During the whaling era, New Bedford's local history was world history, as the far-flung whale ships made the city known in every ocean on the globe.

The principal whaling exhibit consists of: the full-rigged half-scale 89-foot model of the New Bedford whaling bark *Lagoda,* which may be boarded; the 100-foot Richard Ellis mural of sperm whales; whaling industry tools and artifacts; and displays of waterfront trades that supported the whaling industry.

The exhibit galleries contain: examples from the permanent collections of scrimshaw, painting, prints, ship models; exhibits pertaining to life in New Bedford and Old Dartmouth; "The World of the Whaleman," featuring two sections of the 1848 Russell-Purrington "Panorama of a Whaling Voyage Round the World"; and changing exhibits of varied nature.

The library contains a permanent collection of over 15,000 books, pamphlets, maps, charts, broadsides, and periodicals, as well as 1,800 reels of microfilm and access to 15,000 photographic negatives. There are 750 feet of manuscripts including over 1,100 logbooks and journals. (Library users should call in advance of their visit to arrange an appointment.)

Activities
Guided tours, lectures, films, gallery talks, and education programs. A whaling film is shown in a large theater in the summer at 10:30 A.M. and 1:30 P.M.

Admission
Entry fee. Open Monday–Saturday and holidays, 9 A.M.–5 P.M., Sunday, 1 P.M.–5 P.M. Closed Thanksgiving, Christmas, and New Year's Day.

NEWBURYPORT
Custom House Maritime Museum of Newburyport

Custom House Maritime Museum
25 Water Street
P.O. Box 306
Newburyport, MA 01950
(508) 462-8681

Location
Newburyport is situated forty miles north of Boston on the south shore of the Merrimack River. Take I-95 to Rte. 1, bearing east three miles into the town.

Highlights
Scrimshaw process
Library (100 volumes)
The Chandler's Gift Shop

General Information
Custom House Maritime Museum of Newburyport, founded in 1969, is located in a classic revival-style customhouse built in 1835. Exhibits pertain to U.S. Coast Guard and maritime history, foreign trade, and shipbuilding. Collections, spanning a period of

300 years, include: artifacts relating to the maritime history of Merrimack Valley; objects brought back in the 1800s from the Orient, Europe, and the South Seas; shipbuilding and navigational tools and instruments; and U.S. Coast Guard artifacts.

The library contains books on maritime and naval history, the works of John P. Marquand, and Newburyport history. It is available for use on the premises by historical and genealogical researchers.

Activities
Tours, lectures, gallery talks, concerts, and educational programs

Admission
"Nominal Customs Tarriff." Memberships are available. Open Monday–Saturday, 10 A.M.–4:30 P.M., Sunday, 1 P.M.–4 P.M., mid-March–January; Monday–Friday, 10 A.M.–4 P.M. the rest of the year.

NORTH TRURO
Truro Historical Society Museum

Truro Historical Society Museum
Highland Road
North Truro, MA 02652
(508) 487-3397

Location
From Boston, take SR-3 south forty-one miles to Rte. 6. Head east to Cape Cod, traveling sixty miles to North Truro.

Highlights
Ship models

General Information
Truro Historical Society Museum has a collection of artifacts from the town's historical past including shipwreck mementos, whaling gear, ship models, seventeenth-century firearms, pirates' chests, and period rooms.

Admission
Open Monday–Saturday, 10 A.M.–4 P.M., mid–June–mid–September.

PLYMOUTH
Plimoth Plantation

Plimoth Plantation
1627 Pilgrim Village
P.O. Box 1620
Plymouth, MA 02360
(508) 746-1622

Location
From Boston, take SR-3 the forty miles southeast to Plymouth. Follow Rte. 3A to Plimoth Plantation at the *Mayflower*.

Highlights
A living museum of seventeenth-century Plymouth
The *Mayflower II* (replica ship)
Library (4,000 volumes)

General Information
Plimoth Plantation, founded in 1947, is an outdoor living history museum. Collections include: seventeenth-century English and native American artifacts; house furnishings; tools; arms and armor; and a reproduction of a 1627 pilgrim village and Wampanoag Indian settlement, where costumed personnel re-create life from that period.

Also located at Plimoth Plantation is the reproduction *Mayflower II,* the type of ship that brought the pilgrims to the New World in 1620. Costumed guides portray passengers and crew and describe life aboard the ship. Exhibits recount the history of the *Mayflower*.

Activities
The library contains imprints and manuscripts available for use by appointment. Additionally, there are a theater, a picnic area, lectures, films, demonstrations, first-person narrative of daily life in Plymouth three centuries ago, education programs, and tours of the *Mayflower II*.

Admission
Entry fee. Memberships are available.

Mayflower II: open daily, 9 A.M.–5 P.M., 26 March–June; daily 9 A.M.–6:30 P.M., mid-June–August; daily, 9 A.M.–5 P.M., September–November. Village: open daily, 9 A.M.–5 P.M., April–November.

SALEM
Peabody Museum

Peabody Museum
East India Square
Salem, MA 01970
(508) 745-1876/9500

Location
Salem is only nineteen miles northeast of Boston on Rte. 1A. The museum is downtown off Charter Street.

Highlights
Navigational instruments of Nathaniel Bowditch
Scrimshaw
American Neptune (quarterly)
Library (100,000 volumes)

General Information
In 1799 Salem's sea captains founded the Peabody Museum, our country's oldest continuing museum. They also created the East India Marine Society. One can study early methods of navigation and the development of navigational instruments, focusing on Nathaniel Bowditch, Salem resident and author of the *American Practical Navigator.*

The museum contains the maritime history of New England, including marine paintings, ship models, figureheads, scrimshaw, whaling gear, nautical tools, and instruments. Exhibits on the Orient and the natural history of New England and the China Trade are also on display.

The library contains maritime history, ethnology of non-European peoples, natural history of Essex County, paintings, prints, ship models, charts, and arts and crafts. In addition, there are reproductions of museum objects, a reading room, and a laboratory of prehistoric archaeology.

Activities
Guided tours, lectures, gallery talks, and education programs

Admission
Entry fee. Memberships are available. Open Monday–Wednesday, Friday and Saturday, 10 A.M.–5 P.M., Thursday, 10 A.M.–9 P.M., Sunday, noon–5 P.M.

Salem Maritime National Historic Site

Salem Maritime National Historic Site
Custom House
174 Derby Street
Salem, MA 01970
(617) 744-4323

Location
Salem is nineteen miles northeast of Boston on Rte. 1A.

Highlights
Historical waterfront commercial district which includes: Derby Wharf, warehouses, the Custom House, the Scale House, the West India Goods Store, Derby House, Hawkes House, Narbonne-Hale House, and the Lighthouse.

General Information
Salem Maritime National Historic Site, founded in 1938, is a nine-acre historic site operated by the National Park Service. It includes Derby Wharf—once center of Salem shipping; Derby House—home of Elias Hasket Derby, a Salem merchant and the first U.S. millionaire; U.S. Customhouse; and a commercial and residential village from the days when Salem was a seaport rivaling Boston and New York.

The wharves at Salem Maritime National Historic Site stretch out into the salt waters of Salem Harbor, testifying to the city's former dependence on the sea. The once busy wharves and the buildings facing the harbor are remnants of the shipping industry that prospered in Massachusetts Bay's oldest seaport well into the last century. In its prime there were fifteen buildings on Derby Wharf.

Admission
No entry fee. Open daily, 8:30 A.M.–5 P.M., September–June; 8:30 A.M.–6 P.M., July–Labor Day.

SCITUATE
Scituate Lighthouse

Scituate Lighthouse
Scituate Historical Society
121 Maple Street
Scituate, MA 02066
(617) 545-0474/1083

Location
South of Cohassett near Boston on the Atlantic coast, Scituate is accessible from SR-3A. Go to the harbor, then take Jericho Road to Lighthouse Road.

Highlights
Lighthouse
Historic structures
Library (300 volumes)

General Information
Scituate Lighthouse was founded in 1810. Here, Abigail (fifteen) and Rebecca (sixteen), the daughters of the keeper, took up a fife and a drum and frightened away British soldiers who planned to burn the town in the War of 1812. (The fife is on view during tours.)

Collections include general and early colonial information; textiles and costumes; Indian artifacts; General Lafayette's coach; Chief Justice William Cushing's "one-hoss" shay; other coaches; books and documents; early farming and cobbler's tools; a sail loft; and sail-making and shipbuilding tools.

Historic structures and artifacts on site are: a 1640 old Stockbridge gristmill that grinds corn during tours; the 1700s Mann farmhouse; Spanish treasure; the 1902 Lawson Tower; a 1675 homestead and well with special Samuel Woodworth (author of "The Old Oaken Bucket") memorabilia; a 1797 library and museum; a 1795 barn; a 1636 cattle pound; and an 1893 little red schoolhouse. The library contains history, genealogy, and town records.

Activities
Guided tours, lectures, education programs, weaving demonstrations on a 275-year-old loom, and spinning in Cudworth House. Bells are rung in the Lawson Tower.

Admission
Entry fee. Memberships are available. Cudworth House and Mann Farmhouse: open Wednesday–Saturday, 2 P.M.–5 P.M., mid-June–mid-September. Little Red Schoolhouse (on 43 Cudworth Road): open Monday–Saturday, 10 A.M.–4 P.M., mid-June–mid-September. Genealogical library is open to groups by appointment only.

SHARON
Kendall Whaling Museum

Kendall Whaling Museum
27 Everett Street
P.O. Box 297
Sharon, MA 02067
(617) 784-5642

Location
Sharon is twenty miles south of Boston just off I-95. Take either exit 8 or 10 to Rte. 1 for access to SR-27 into the village.

Highlights
The annual whaling symposium
Ship models
The KWM Newsletter
Library

General Information
A world-class international collection of artworks, maritime artifacts, and curiosities that spans six centuries and seven continents is exquisitely set in the New England countryside. The Kendall Whaling Museum was established in 1956. It houses nine of the world's most beautiful maritime galleries, with a fine international collection of nautical art, history, and ethnology. The museum is particularly renowned for its sumptuous Dutch and Flemish paintings, engravings, and Delft tiles from the Age of Rembrandt. Also displayed are British and Continental whaling artworks; Japanese paintings and prints; Pacific Ocean, Eskimo, Northwest Coast Indian, and other tribal art; a fully equipped Yankee whaleboat, ship models, and whaling gear from New England's classic Age of Sail—including the world's finest collection of scrimshaw.

Activities
Annual whaling symposium each October

Admission
Entry fee. Open Tuesday–Saturday, 10 A.M.–5 P.M. Other times by appointment.

WELLFLEET
Historical Society Museum

Historical Society Museum
Main Street
Wellfleet, MA 02667
(508) 349-9157

Location
From Boston take SR-3 south to Rte. 6 (forty-one miles). Travel east to Cape Cod, then an additional forty-one miles to Wellfleet Harbor at the Cape's northern tip.

Highlights
Old Cape Cod history

General Information
The Historical Society Museum has marine items, whaling tools, Marconi (radio) memorabilia, needlecraft, and a photograph collection. Nearby Rider House is restored and depicts life on old Cape Cod through displays of early farming and carpentry tools, and an herb garden.

Admission
No entry fee. Open Tuesday–Saturday, 2 P.M.–5 P.M., late June–Labor day.

RHODE ISLAND

BRISTOL
Herreshoff Marine Museum and Monument

Herreshoff Marine Museum
P.O. Box 450
7 Burnside Street
Bristol, RI 02809
(401) 253-5000

Location
Bristol lies approximately twelve miles southeast of Providence. The museum and monument are near Mt. Hope Bridge on Rte. 114.

Highlights
Exhibits of Herreshoff yachts and steam engines
Photographs and other memorabilia

General Information
The Herreshoff Marine Museum, founded in 1971, displays yachts, steam engines, fittings, photographs, and memorabilia commemorating the unique accomplishments of the Herreshoff Manufacturing Company, which existed from 1863 to 1946—the "Golden Age of Yachting." John Brown Herreshoff founded the company in 1863, and in 1878 he took his younger brother, Nathanael Greene, into partnership. After attending Massachusetts Insti-

The graceful lines of the *Elizabeth Howard,* shown on a starboard tack in the Gloucester Races on 27 August 1923. (Rosenfeld Collections, Mystic Seaport Museum, Inc.)

tute of Technology, Nat was employed by the famed Corliss Engine Works in Providence for nine years. Upon joining his brother's firm of boatbuilders, he concentrated initially on designing steam vessels.

In the early 1890s Nat turned to designing sailing yachts; the creation of these vessels—of all sizes and descriptions—occupied most of the rest of his professional career. Yachts of his design, built at the family's yard, defended the America's Cup six times from 1893 to 1920, and the Herreshoff Manufacturing Company also built the Cup defenders of 1930 and 1934.

Activities
A rendezvous every three years of Herreshoff-designed boats (next one scheduled for 1990), annual summer waterfront clambakes, lectures, and workshops

NEWPORT
Museum of Yachting

Museum of Yachting
Fort Adams State Park
P.O. Box 129
Newport, RI 02840
(401) 847-1018

Location
Newport lies nineteen miles south of Fall River, Massachusetts, on SR-24. The Museum of Yachting is at Fort Adams State Park, the landing for the Newport to Block Island ferry.

Highlights
The *Shamrock V* (sailboat)
Small-craft collection
Hall of Fame (sponsored by British Oxygen Corporation)
America's Cup galleries

General Information
The Museum of Yachting has recently acquired the *Shamrock V,* the last of Sir Thomas Lipton's contenders for the America's Cup.

The 130-foot J-boat, in addition to being a museum exhibit, tours up and down the East Coast. The museum's developers envisioned a facility where visitors could learn something about yachting history, technology, and the people who have been instrumental in its evolution. The museum exhibits include the America's Cup, the Hall of Fame for Singlehanded Sailors, the Phil Weld Library, the Golden Age of Yachting, and the Great Designers. Other craft include a Bris "amphibie" sailing craft fifteen feet in length.

Activities
An annual classic regatta on Labor Day weekend; a yacht auction every June; an unlimited regatta in September; winter educational program; and a School of Yacht Restoration.

Admission
Entry fee. Open Monday–Saturday, 10 A.M.–5 P.M., 15 May–31 October.

Naval War College Museum

Naval War College Museum
Coasters Harbor Island
Newport, RI 02841-5010
(401) 841-4052/1317

Location
From I-95, exit onto SR-24/114 heading south. After thirteen miles exit west onto Admiral Kalbfus Road to the Naval War College at Coasters Harbor Island, Newport.

Highlights
History of naval warfare
History of the navy in Narragansett Bay
Library

General Information
Founded in 1978, the Naval War College Museum exhibits a collection of art, artifacts, imprints, and prints on the history of naval

warfare and the navy in the Narragansett Bay region. The history of the "art and science" of naval warfare, as chiefly studied at the Naval War College through the years, is the principal exhibit theme of the museum. In its broadest application, this encompasses theories and concepts of sea power, international and maritime law, foreign policy formulation, diplomacy, and naval operations. More specifically, the focus is on naval power and the professional implementation of strategic and tactical objectives.

Exhibits explain the importance of the sea as a factor in the formulation of national policy objectives and as the arena wherein decisions are wrought through diplomacy and trial by arms. In addition, exhibits tell the story of the long and eventful relationship of the navy with Narragansett Bay and the people of Rhode Island.

A small library of books on museology and related fields is available on the premises, as is the archive and reading room.

Activities
Guided tours

Admission
No entry fee. Open Monday–Friday, 10 A.M.–4 P.M., Saturdays and Sundays, noon–4 P.M., June–September.

PROVIDENCE

Alfred S. Brownell Collection of Atlantic Coast Fishing Craft Models

Alfred S. Brownell Collection
Providence Public Library
225 Washington Street
Providence, RI 02903-3283
(401) 455-8000/8021

Location
This particular collection is housed in the Providence Public Library, downtown near I-95.

Highlights
Small-craft collection
Logbook collection
Scrimshaw
Library

General Information
The Alfred S. Brownell Collection of Atlantic Coast Fishing Craft Models comprises eleven ship models of Atlantic coast fishing craft. They were presented to the library about 1950 by Mr. Brownell, himself a marine historian and one of the most highly regarded model-boatbuilders. The eleven distinct types of fishing craft were evolved as early as the colonial times to meet the needs of men fishing in such diverse areas as the sheltered waters of Long Island Sound, the stormy ocean off the coast of Maine, and the shallow oyster beds of the Chesapeake Bay.

Thousands of hours were required to prepare scale drawings and to produce each model. The fishing fleet contained in the collection includes a Block Island Double Ender, a Chesapeake Bay Bugeye and Skipjack, a Colonial Fishing Schooner, an Eastport Pinkey, a Friendship Sloop, a Gloucester Sloop, a Maine Pinkey, a New Haven Sharpie, a Quoddy, and a Tancook Whaler.

Most of the collection is displayed on level B of the library. In addition, the Nicholson Whaling Collection of over 1,000 whaling logs, books, and seventy-seven pieces of scrimshaw is in the Special Collections Department.

Activities
Library available for research

Admission
Entry fee. Fishing Craft Models Collection: Open Monday, Tuesday, Thursday, and Friday, 9:30 A.M.–noon, 1 P.M.–5 P.M., 15 June–mid-September. Closed national holidays. Nicholson Whaling Collection: Open Monday, Tuesday, Thursday, and Friday, 9:30 A.M.–1 P.M., 2 P.M.–5 P.M., year-round. Closed Saturdays, Sundays, and holidays. (Phone ahead: 401-455-8021.)

Providence (Replica Sloop)

Providence
Seaport '76 Foundation
P.O. Box 76
Newport, RI 02840
(401) 846-1776

Location
The replica is moored on the Providence River off I-95 in the city.

Highlights
The *Providence* (replica sloop)

General Information
The fighting craft of the American Revolution were built by the Providence merchant John Brown, and until 1775 they engaged in highly prosperous trade with ports in the West Indies. Rhode Island, the first colony to organize a navy, commissioned the *Katy* (later renamed the *Providence*) to confront British customs ships in Narragansett Bay. She was the first ship commissioned into the Continental Navy. She was also the first command of John Paul Jones, the first ship to land U.S. Marines on foreign soil, the first ship to fly the U.S. flag on foreign soil, and the most successful ship of the Colonial Navy in the Revolutionary War (over forty captures or sinkings).

Five months after the first at-sea fight of the Revolution, in May 1775, the *Katy* was renamed the *Providence*. She was Rhode Island's initial contribution to the Continental Navy. John Paul Jones described her four years of fighting as follows: "Her's is a record unmatched by any other Continental vessel, and her quarter deck served as a proving ground for some of the greatest Revolutionary captains." She was burned by her own crew in Penobscot Bay, Maine, in August 1779 to avoid capture by the British.

Today from Narrangansett Bay comes a fully operational 110-foot reproduction of the *Providence*, the ship that sailed there two hundred years ago.

Activities
Available for charter, visits to patriotic or historical events in U.S. seaports, and the American Sail Training program

Admission
Call or write this sailing museum for information about their opening hours.

CONNECTICUT

BRIDGEPORT
HMS *Rose* (Replica Ship)

HMS *Rose* Foundation
Captain's Cove Seaport
1 Bostwick Avenue
Bridgeport, CT 06605
(203) 335-1433

Location
Upon arrival in Bridgeport on I-95, exit onto Black Rock Turnpike. Follow the turnpike to Captain's Cove Seaport in Bridgeport.

Highlights
HMS *Rose* (world's largest active wooden sailing vessel)

General Information
Built in Nova Scotia in 1970, the HMS *Rose* is a replica of the 1757 British frigate that played a prominent part in the Seven Years War and the American Revolution.

The new *Rose* was built essentially from the same plans as her predecessor, which was launched from the renowned Smith and Rhuland Shipyard, Lunenburg, Nova Scotia. Originally berthed in Newport, Rhode Island, the *Rose* is now the largest operational wooden sailing vessel in the world. Experienced crew give visitors a guided tour and lectures, and exhibits illustrate the rich maritime history of colonial Connecticut.

In 1990 the *Rose* became U.S. Coast Guard–certified as the largest sailing school vessel in America.

Activities
Dockside tours when the *Rose* is in port, daily, noon–5 P.M., May–October; educational day sail classes beginning spring 1990. Call or write the foundation for more information

Admission
Entry fee.

ESSEX
The Connecticut River Museum

The Connecticut River Museum
Steamboat Dock
P.O. Box 261
Essex, CT 06426
(203) 767-8269

Location
Essex is located off SR-9, three miles north of the I-95 interchange. The museum sits at the foot of Main Street on the Connecticut River steamboat dock site in Essex Village.

Highlights
The *American Turtle* (first submarine)
Ship models
Steamboat Log (newsletter)
Thomas A. Steven Library (a research facility)

General Information
The Connecticut River Foundation, founded in 1974, displays a working reproduction of the *American Turtle,* the first submarine, invented by David Bushness in 1775. Permanent exhibits include valley archaeology; Lay's Wharf (c. 1650); small-craft exhibits on river hunting, fishing, yachting; steamboating; brownstone schooners, models, and paintings of the Revolutionary War and the 1812 burning of the fleet at Essex.

Activities
Guided tours, lecture series, films, formally organized education programs, Traditional Vessel Weekend, changing exhibits, and a permanent collection.

Admission
Entry fee. Memberships are available, which may include docking privileges. Open Tuesday–Sunday, 10 A.M.–5 P.M., April–December. Closed national holidays.

GROTON
Nautilus Memorial

Nautilus Memorial
Submarine Force Library and Museum
Naval Submarine Base New London
P.O. Box 571
Groton, CT 06349-5000
(203) 449-4276 Toll Free: 1 (800) 343-0079 (tape recording)

Location
Groton is forty-five miles east of New Haven. The submarine and museum are off Rte. 12 near the entrance to the Naval Submarine Base.

Highlights
The USS *Nautilus* (1955—first nuclear-powered submarine in the U.S. Navy)
Submarine periscopes

General Information

The *Nautilus* and the Submarine Force Library and Museum (founded in 1964) are located outside the main gate of the naval base. The museum is a repository for the records and history of the U.S. Submarine Force, from its humble beginnings at the turn of the century to the modern navy.

In the museum entrance is an eleven-foot model of the fictional Captain Nemo's *Nautilus* from Jules Verne's *20,000 Leagues Under the Sea.* The museum displays working periscopes, an authentic submarine control room, and an extensive wall of ship models that depict the development of the U.S. Submarine Force.

The collection of historic submarines includes the first nuclear-powered submarine *Nautilus* (1954); the Japanese Kairyu and Type A; the Italian *Maile;* the German *Seehund;* and an early American research submarine, Simon Lake's *Explorer.* Other collections include pictures, plaques, battle flags, paintings, brow canvases, submarine parts, medals and personal memorabilia from submariners, 50,000 photographs of submarines and related subjects, films, blueprints, technical manuals, letters, papers, and diaries.

Activities

Self-guided tours of the world's first nuclear-powered vessel, the *Nautilus;* working models of navy periscopes; a submarine control room and two mini-theaters with five-minute films depicting the growth and history of the U.S. Submarine Force and the USS *Nautilus.*

Admission

No entry fee.

Museum: open Wednesday–Monday, 9 A.M.–5 P.M., mid-April–September; Wednesday–Sunday, 9 A.M.–3:30 P.M., mid-October–mid-April.

Library: open Monday, Wednesday, Thursday, and Friday, 8:30 A.M.–3:30 P.M., by appointment only. Closed Thanksgiving, Christmas, and New Year's Day.

(The *Nautilus,* Museum, and Library are closed every Tuesday and five days every quarter.)

MYSTIC
Mystic Seaport Museum

Mystic Seaport Museum
50 Greenmanville Avenue
Mystic, CT 06355-0990
(203) 572-0711

Location
Mystic is seven miles east of New London along the Mystic River on SR-27.

Highlights
Boardable nineteenth-century vessels
Ship models
Scrimshaw
Boatbuilding
The *Log* (quarterly)
The Windrose (newsletter)
Library (research and archives of American yachting and boating)

General Information
Through Mystic's historic homes, shops, and trade buildings, the visitor may gain an understanding of life in a seaport during the mid-nineteenth century. The last of the wooden whaling ships, the *Charles W. Morgan,* the 1882 training ship *Joseph Conrad,* and the fishing schooner *L. A. Dunton* may be boarded by visitors. More than 100 other ships and boats are on display in the museum (founded in 1929).

Ship models, scrimshaw, figureheads, small boats, and other relics trace the history of ships, shipbuilding, and maritime activities. The R. J. Schaefer Building features changing exhibits of paintings and artifacts. There is also a children's museum where youngsters may play with toys, clothing, and games popular in the 1800s. Special children's programs and tours are offered in July and August (check locally for schedule).

Visitors may watch skilled shipwrights restore historic vessels in the seaport's preservation shipyard. Sea chanty concerts, as well as demonstrations of fireplace cooking, boatbuilding, sail

The *Joseph Conrad,* shown here in a 1937 photograph, is a mainstay at the Mystic Seaport Museum. Hundreds of young people take advantage of the Mariner Training Programs, learning sailing and proper seamanship at the seaport. This image was acquired in honor of Franz Schenider by the seaport. (Rosenfeld Collections, Mystic Seaport Museum, Inc.)

setting, and maritime arts, are given. Craftspeople may be seen working in some shops. A planetarium offers daily shows.

The museum has purchased the entire Rosenfeld collection of photographs, which comprises more than one million images, documents more than 100 years of maritime and yachting history, and is the single largest collection of marine photographs in the world.

The seaport provides opportunities for college-level maritime studies. The Munson Institute conducts graduate-level courses during the summer months, while undergraduate maritime studies courses are offered through the Williams College/Mystic Seaport Program during the academic year.

Admission
Entry fee. Memberships are available. Museum open daily, 9 A.M.–5 P.M., 1 May–31 October; 9 A.M.–4 P.M. the rest of the year. Closed Christmas, and open limited hours on Thanksgiving, Christmas Eve, and New Year's Eve.

NEW LONDON
U.S. Coast Guard Museum

U.S. Coast Guard Museum
U.S. Coast Guard Academy
New London, CT 06320-4195
(203) 444-8511

Location
New London is fifty miles east of New Haven. In town, follow signs to the U.S. Coast Guard Academy.

Highlights
The *Eagle* (training bark)
Library (150,000 volumes)
Gift shop in Visitor's Center

General Information
The U.S. Coast Guard Museum in Waesche Hall was founded in 1967. Collections include ship and airplane models; paintings and artifacts; flags and figureheads relating to the U.S. Coast Guard and its predecessors—the Revenue-Cutter Service, Lighthouse Service, and Lifesaving Service—and the bark *Eagle*.

The *Eagle* celebrated her fiftieth anniversary in 1986 by leading the parade of the world's sail training ships in New York Harbor on the Fourth of July. She also marked the beginning of her fifth decade as the Coast Guard Academy's principal sail training vessel.

Launched at the well-known German shipyard of Blohm and Voss on 13 June 1936, and originally named *Horst Wessel,* she is one of three similar bark-rigged sailing vessels built by that yard in the late thirties for the German Navy's sail training program. The *Eagle* was taken by the United States in war reparations at the end of 1945. She was delivered to her U.S. Coast Guard crew in Bremerhaven in January 1946, after which she spent five months being refitted and prepared for her transatlantic voyage. The *Eagle* arrived in her new home port of New London in July 1946.

A tradition of square-rig cadet training vessels began with the topsail schooner *Dobbin* in 1877. In 1878 a new bark, the *S. P. Chase,* was built as a replacement, serving to 1906. Then the *Itasca,* a steam vessel with auxiliary sail, served to 1920, followed by the *Alexander Hamilton,* formerly the USS *Vicksburg*. In December 1941 the Danish full-rigged training ship *Danmark* was used to train cadets in wartime. The *Danmark* was replaced by the *Eagle,* which continues to serve as the training vessel for the Coast Guard Academy. The Academy, founded in 1876, conducts a full four-year educational program leading to a B.S. degree. Training cruises (often to European ports) are scheduled in the summer months.

Admission
No entry fee. Pavilion and museum open Monday–Friday, 10 A.M.–5 P.M., 1 May–31 October; museum only open daily, 8 A.M.–4 P.M., the rest of the year. Closed national holidays. If the training bark *Eagle* is in port, she may be boarded.

NORWALK
The Maritime Center at Norwalk

The Maritime Center at Norwalk
10 North Water Street
South Norwalk, CT 06854
(203) 852-0700

Location
Norwalk is just six miles east of Stamford. The center is near South Norwalk's recently renovated historic Washington Street. It is a short distance from I-95 and a brief walk from the AMTRAK/Metro North railroad station.

Highlights
The Aquarium: Sharks, seals, and sea life indigenous to Long Island Sound
The Maritime Hall: Boatbuilding, interactive video displays, and oystering exhibits
IMAX Theater: "Image Maximum" viewing experience

General Information
The Maritime Center at Norwalk, founded in 1988, is devoted to the maritime history and marine life of Long Island Sound. The Maritime Center is home to the research vessel *Oceanic,* the historic oystering sloop *Hope,* and *The Glory Days,* an elegant steam tender.

The center makes renewed and appropriate use of some nineteenth-century factory buildings on the west bank of the Norwalk River. The center's history exhibits focus on the industrial and maritime life of the Connecticut coast. Interactive exhibits demonstrate the dynamics of sailing, navigation, and computerized boat design.

Activities
Marine science programs, field studies, and IMAX films

Admission
Call or write the center for information about their opening hours.

STONINGTON
Old Lighthouse Museum

Old Lighthouse Museum
7 Water Street
Stonington, CT 06378
(203) 535-1440 (summer); 536-7896 (winter)

Location
Stonington is fifteen miles west of New London at the south end of Water Street.

Highlights
Lighthouse
Ship models

General Information
Old Lighthouse Museum, founded in 1927, is housed in a stone lighthouse built in 1840. Exhibits include ship models, whaling gear, firearms, stoneware, and early maritime portraits. Also displayed are furniture, silver and pewter, and utensils at Whitehall; seventeenth- and eighteenth-century historical treasures of the town including whaling and War of 1812 relics; and manuscript collections. (The Pequot Indians were dominant in this area until their defeat in 1637, when the first white settlement was established.)

Activities
Guided tours, lectures, formal education programs, and permanent and temporary exhibits

Admission
Entry fee. Memberships are available. Open Tuesday–Sunday, 1 P.M.–4:30 P.M., May–October.

TWO

MID-ATLANTIC

NEW YORK (LOWER)

CROTON-ON-HUDSON
National Maritime Historical Society

National Maritime Historical Society
132 Maple Street
Croton-on-Hudson, NY 10520
(914) 271-2177

Location
Croton-on-Hudson is on the east side of the river, approximately forty miles north of New York City in Westchester County, off Rte. 9.

Highlights
Sea History (quarterly publication)
Sea History Gazette (biweekly publication)

General Information
The National Maritime Historical Society, founded in 1963, brings America's seafaring past to life through research, archaeological expeditions, and ship preservation efforts.

The Society is the American arm of the World Ship Trust, an international group that saves ships of historic importance. *Sea History* is the primary vehicle used to describe maritime heritage through its many articles on ships, naval architecture, artifacts, etc. (There is no on-site museum facility.)

CUDDEBACKVILLE
Neversink Valley Area Museum/D and H Canal Park

Neversink Valley Area Museum
D and H Canal Site
P.O. Box 263
Cuddebackville, NY 12729
(914) 754-8870

Location

The Delaware and Hudson (D and H) Canal is on Rte. 209 about ten miles north of Port Jervis, which is on I-84 at the juncture of New York, Pennsylvania, and New Jersey.

Highlights

One mile of the D and H Canal
Six canal-era structures
John A. Roebling's Neversink aqueduct
Guided towpath tours
Gift shop

General Information

Neversink Valley Area Museum/D and H Canal Park, founded in 1963, was established to acquire and restore historical sites within the area and to preserve in them the artifacts and memorabilia of the past.

Remnants of a transportation era when the canal was king may be visited. Those early days are being re-created by the museum in whose collections are examples of the household tools used by the families that lived along the waterway. In the early 1800s the United States was facing an energy shortage. To transport anthracite coal (an important fuel), the D and H canal was opened in 1828. It spanned the 108 miles on the Hudson River from Honesdale, Pennsylvania, to an area near Kingston, New York. The trip took ten days by barge and included 108 locks.

The D and H Canal Park comprises nearly 300 acres, and the museum displays artifacts, maps, photographs, and other memorabilia of the period of canal usage, including a blacksmith's house and a carpenter's house.

Admission

Entry fee. Open Thursday–Sunday, 1 P.M.–4 P.M., April–December; Saturdays and Sundays only, 11 A.M.–4 P.M., January–March.

EAST HAMPTON
East Hampton Town Marine Museum

East Hampton Town Marine Museum
101 Main Street
East Hampton, NY 11937
(516) 324-6850 or 267-6544

Location
From New York City take I-495 east on Long Island to SR-46. Follow that south three miles to SR-27. Head east on it to Atlantic Avenue in Amagansett (East Hampton's neighbor to the north).

Highlights
Shore whaling, farmers, fishermen, and commercial fishing of the area
Edwards whaleboat and Dominy whaleboat
Boat shop on Three Mile Harbor

General Information
East Hampton Town Marine Museum, founded in 1966, is located high on Bluff Road in Amagansett in a former World War II navy barracks that overlooks the Atlantic. From its vantage point you can see the offshore dragger fleet from Montauk, seiners working their dories through the surf, yachts sailing up the coast, wildlife roaming the dunes, and, of course, people walking the beach, swimming, or just looking out to sea.

The Town Marine Museum tells the story of a town and its 300-year relationship to the sea. Its unique perspective is not that of the historian or scholar, although its exhibits are characterized by thoughtful interpretation of historical research. Rather, it looks at the people who work on the water every day of their lives to feed their families and their nation. When you see the museum's dioramas, which depict early whaling and modern fishing, you will be seeing the east end of Long Island through the eyes of the commercial fishermen who live there.

Activities
Main-floor, west, and top-floor galleries, plus stairwell photography

Admission
Entry fee. Memberships are available. Open Tuesday–Sunday, 10:30 A.M.–5 P.M., 1 July–Labor Day; Saturdays and Sundays, 10 A.M.–5 P.M., 1–30 June and after Labor Day–30 September. Other times by appointment.

HIGH FALLS
Delaware and Hudson Canal Museum

Delaware and Hudson Canal Museum
Mohonk Road
High Falls, NY 12440
(914) 687-9311

Location
High Falls is twenty-five miles north of Poughkeepsie. Coming from the north on the New York Thruway, take exit 19 south onto Rte. 209. Turn east onto Rte. 213 to High Falls. Coming from the south on the New York Thruway, take exit 18 onto Rte. 299. At New Paltz turn north onto Rte. 32 to Rosendale. At Rosendale turn west onto Rte. 213 into High Falls.

Highlights
Exhibits of canal artifacts and detailed dioramas
Canal history
Working-scale model of a canal lock

General Information
Delaware and Husdon (D and H) Canal Museum, founded in 1966, seeks to inform the public of the great significance of the canal and its related communities; to provide a library and archival facility on the canal and its related industries; and to promote the maintenance and restoration of the extant parts of the canal.

The D and H Canal Historical Society is actively engaged in restoration projects. Through the efforts of the society, locks 16, 17, 18, 19, and 20 and the abutments of the two aqueducts in High Falls, plus the water-filled section of the canal between Alligerville and Accord, have been designated national historic landmarks.

The canal operated from 1828 to 1898, transporting coal on a 108-mile journey on the Hudson River from Hanesdale, Pennsylvania, to Kingston, New York. It was then shipped downriver to New York City. The museum offers a revealing glimpse of what life was like when horses and mules pulled canal boats along the D and H Canal route and through its 108 locks.

Admission
No entry fee. Memberships are available.

Open Thursday–Monday, 11 A.M.–5 P.M., Sunday, 1 P.M.–5 P.M., 30 May–Labor Day; Saturday, 11 A.M.–5 P.M., and Sunday, 1 P.M.–5 P.M., May, September, and October.

HUNTINGTON
Whaling Museum Society

Whaling Museum Society, Inc.
Main Street
P.O. Box 25
Cold Spring Harbor, NY 11724
(516) 367-3418

Location
Take I-95 east from New York City the forty-five miles to SR-110. Travel north six miles to Huntington (just two miles east of Cold Spring Harbor on Rte. 25A).

Highlights
A nineteenth-century whaleboat
Scrimshaw
A Whaling Account (newsletter)
Museum store

General Information
Between the years 1836 and 1862, the town of Cold Spring Harbor supported a fleet of nine whaling vessels. Their voyages lasted between one and five years, sometimes taking them as far away as the Pacific Arctic. The oil secured by these stout vessels helped keep American homes illuminated and its industrial machinery running smoothly.

The Whaling Museum Society, founded in 1936, displays a fully equipped whaleboat from the brig *Daisy,* whaling implements, marine paintings, ship models, a diorama of Cold Spring Harbor as a whaling port in 1850, and a permanent exhibit on Long Island's whaling industry, called "Mark Well the Whale!" The single largest group of objects consists of 700 scrimshawed items produced by whalers of the nineteenth century.

In 1989, a new gallery opened where a collection of paintings and artifacts that trace Cold Spring Harbor's illustrious past are presented. The museum also supports marine mammal conservation through its education programs and exhibits.

Activities
In-service workshops, tours, outreach lectures, and films

Admission
Open Tuesday–Sunday, 11 A.M.–5 P.M., year-round. Closed Thanksgiving, Christmas, and New Year's Day.

HYDE PARK
Franklin D. Roosevelt Library and Museum

Franklin D. Roosevelt Library and Museum
259 Albany Post Road
Hyde Park, NY 12538
(914) 229-8114

Location
Hyde Park is just 4 miles north of Poughkeepsie on Rte. 9 (approximately 100 miles north of New York City).

Highlights
Library (45,000 volumes) and archives (sixteen million pages of manuscripts)
Museum store

General Information
The Franklin D. Roosevelt Library and Museum, founded in 1939 by a joint resolution of Congress, was the first of seven presi-

dential libraries. The museum, open to the public, contains displays on the lives, careers, and interests of both President and Mrs. Franklin D. Roosevelt. "America on the Seas," an exhibit of materials from the President's personal collections, depicts America's naval and maritime history during the Age of Sail. The President's naval/marine collections include ship models, books, artifacts, memorabilia, prints, paintings, photos, letters, logs, and state documents. (The library section is open only to researchers.)

Admission
Entry fee (includes admission to the Roosevelt Home). Open daily, 9 A.M.–5 P.M., year-round. Closed Thanksgiving, Christmas, and New Year's Day.

KINGS POINT

American Merchant Marine Museum at U.S. Merchant Marine Academy

American Merchant Marine Museum
U.S. Merchant Marine Academy
Steamboat Road
Kings Point, NY 11024
(516) 773-5515

Location
Kings Point is in northeast Long Island, just two miles east of the Bronx, facing Long Island Sound.

Highlights
Thirty-five ship models
Steam engine working model
National Maritime Hall of Fame
The Manifest (newsletter)

General Information
The United States is blessed with a rich maritime heritage. From coastal trade vessels of the American colonists to the swift nineteenth-century clipper ships to today's impressive supertankers and containerships, one message is clear—ships made America!

This is the theme of the American Merchant Marine Museum (established in 1979), a national repository and exhibition center for the artifacts, artwork, ship models, and nautical memorabilia depicting America's maritime past.

Many unique and noteworthy items are included in the museum's inventory. Among the over thirty-five ship models regularly on display is a highly valued eighteen-foot-long model of the famous passenger ship SS *Washington*. The highlight of the museum's collection, however, is the Hales Blue Riband Trophy, a magnificent gilt award last won in 1952 by the SS *United States* for the fastest transatlantic crossing ever by a passenger liner.

The museum's National Maritime Hall of Fame is the only such exhibition in the nation dedicated to the great people and great ships of our maritime history. Each year four individuals and four vessels that have made outstanding contributions to the maritime industry are inducted into the Hall.

The *Academy* trains and educates officers for the merchant marine and naval reserve. The seventy-six-acre grounds include the estate of the late Walter Chrysler and the U.S. Merchant Marine Memorial Chapel. The academy's primary responsibility, as stated in federal law, is to train midshipmen (the term applies to the 58 women there as well as the 817 men) to navigate and operate ships. The training leads to licensing as deck officers or engineers.

Admission

No entry fee. Open Tuesday–Wednesday, 11 A.M.–3:30 P.M., Saturdays and Sundays, 1 P.M.–4:30 P.M., year-round. Closed during July and national holidays.

KINGSTON

Hudson River Maritime Center

Hudson River Maritime Center
One Rondout Landing
Kingston, NY 12401
(914) 338-0071

Location

Kingston is situated on the west side of the Hudson River twenty-five miles north of Poughkeepsie. The center sits at Rondout Landing.

Highlights
The *Mathilda* (an 1898 steam tug)
Focs'le News (newsletter)
Library (150 volumes)

General Information
The Hudson River Maritime Center, founded in 1980 at Rondout Landing, was organized as a living museum to preserve the crafts, ships, and exhibits that illustrate the maritime history of the Hudson River region. The area has been a major port on the water for over 300 years. A number of specialized vessels were developed here over the years to fill the transport needs of New York industry, including the steamboats that raced each other up and down the Hudson in a battle for passengers and cargo.

Exhibits include 245 collections containing over 4,033 items, from various boats used in Hudson River traffic to paintings depicting the early era of river use. A stop at the Anton Otto Fischer gallery, where eighteen oil paintings titled "The Focs'le Days" are on display, is a must.

The library collection pertains to steam and sail on the Hudson River and is available to the public.

Activities
Guided tours, lectures, concerts, and library

Admission
Entry fee. Memberships are available. Open Wednesday–Sunday, noon–5 P.M., year-round.

NEW YORK CITY
City Island Museum

City Island Museum
190 Fordham Street
Bronx, NY 10464
(212) 885-1616

Location
The museum is in the Bronx, just east off the Bronx-Pelham Parkway.

Highlights
America's Cup exhibit
City Island history from 1800
Newsletter
Library (150 volumes)

General Information
City Island Museum, founded in 1964, is a nautical historical museum housed in the former P.S. 17, one of the first school buildings of greater New York City (1887). The museum building is listed with the National Historic Trust.

Collections include paintings, photographs, artifacts, documents, and memorabilia from pre-Plymouth landing times to the present. The part played by City Island in the yachting industry and the America's Cup Races and Hell Gate Pilots is emphasized. The library, available for use on the premises, contains information on local history.

Activities
Guided tours, lectures, films, and educational programs

Admission
Entry fee. Memberships are available. Open Sunday, 2 P.M.–5 P.M., and Wednesday, 2 P.M.–4 P.M., year-round. Tours by appointment only.

***Intrepid* Sea-Air-Space Museum**

Intrepid Sea-Air-Space Museum
1 Intrepid Plaza
Pier 86, 46th Street and 12th Avenue
New York, NY 10036
(212) 245-0072/2533

Location
The USS *Intrepid* is docked at New York City's Pier 86, located at 46th Street and 12th Avenue.

Highlights

The USS *Intrepid* (aircraft carrier)
The USS *Growler* (guided missile submarine)
The USS *Edson* (destroyer)
Forty-one aircraft ranging from pre–World War I through modern day on display on flight/hangar decks
Library (5,000 volumes)

General Information

Perhaps no ship in the annals of the U.S. Navy has done more to live up to her name than the USS *Intrepid.* After a gallant thirty-nine-year cruise, the historic ship is now the *Intrepid* Sea-Air-Space Museum, founded in 1982.

The USS *Growler* may also be toured. She is a guided-missile submarine that served the country for six years armed with Regulus missiles, patrolling the western Pacific Ocean as a strategic nuclear defense deterrent during the Belling Bay of Pigs and the Cuban Missile Crisis of the Cold War period.

The USS *Edson,* a Vietnam-era destroyer with the motto "Three Guns, No Waiting," served the country for thirty years. Named for USMC Major General and Congressional Medal of Honor recipient Merritt Austin ("Red Mike") Edson, this ship provided gunfire support during wartime and a training platform for officers and enlisted personnel during times of peace.

Collections include an open flight deck with displays; World War II aircraft; Grumman Avenger; Grumman Hellcat; tools; suspended aircraft; vertical flight vehicles; space flight vehicles; ballistic missiles; and forty-one planes and helicopters ranging from pre–World War I through modern day aviation. A Congressional Medal of Honor Museum is also housed here. Additionally, a six-year-long rotating exhibit dedicated to World War II, including all its significant battles, began with "Poland Invaded."

The 710-foot long hangar deck contains well-crafted exhibits, displays, and photographs. Carrier Operations presentations include: the U.S. Navy Hall, which features the modern peacekeeping navy; Intrepid Hall, which focuses on the *Intrepid* during World War II; Pioneer Hall, a tribute to early aviation; and Technologies Hall, where exhibits and displays present some of the greatest advances in sea, air, and space technology. Other notable exhibit areas include the Combat Information Center, Air Traffic Control, and Undersea Frontier. The library has information pertaining to sea, air, and space, history, and technology.

Activities
Films, educational programs, and special-event halls

Admission
Entry fee. Memberships are available. Open Wednesday–Sunday, 10 A.M.–5 P.M., year-round (last admission at 4 P.M.).

Maritime Industry Museum at Fort Schuyler

Maritime Industry Museum at Fort Schuyler
New York State Maritime College
Fort Schuyler, Throggs Neck
The Bronx, NY 10465
(212) 409-7200/7218

Location
The museum is on the campus of the State University of New York's Maritime College in the Throggs Neck section of the Bronx. Take the Ft. Schuyler exit off I-295.

Highlights
Ship models
Library

General Information
Founded in 1985, the Maritime Industry Museum at Fort Schuyler has various exhibits including displays that depict the development and history of the international merchant marine, related shoreside industries, and ports. The history of the Maritime College is also a part of the museum. Exhibits include marine paintings, watercolors, photographs, and artifacts. There is also a unique collection of twenty-six ship models, from early sailing vessels to modern freighters, tankers, and ocean liners.

The 535-foot training ship *Empire State* (formerly the USNS *Barrett*) is the seventh training ship used by the Maritime College since its founding in 1874. Visitors may tour the ship nine months of the year and the tugs *General Philip Schuyler* (formerly USCGC *Mahoning*) and USCG *Raritan*.

Activities
Vistors may tour the fort and campus grounds

Admission
No entry fee. Open Monday–Friday, 8:30 A.M.–4:30 P.M., year-round. Closed Thanksgiving, Christmas, and New Year's Day.

South Street Seaport Museum

South Street Seaport Museum
207 Front Street
New York, NY 10038
(212) 669-9400

Location
The museum is situated in the lower east side of Manhattan on the East River in an area bounded by South, Front, Pearl, and Dover Streets.

Highlights
Boardable historic vessels
The *Titanic* memorial
Special tours of Manhattan's historic district
Children's center
Library

General Information
South Street Seaport Museum, founded in 1967, is an eleven-block historic area on the East River that was created as a landfill in the late eighteenth century and was the city's bustling seaport in the nineteenth. The brick and granite buildings that line the Belgian block streets were built as shops, warehouses, and counting

The steel four-masted bark *Peking*, built in 1911 for the Laeisz "Flying P" Line in Hamburg, Germany, was in nitrate trade to South America until 1921, when she was turned over to Italy as a World War I reparation. Bought back by Laeisz in 1923, she was sold again to be a training ship—the *Arethusa*—in England. She is now a museum ship at the South Street Seaport in New York City. (Photo: Jerry MacMullen Library, Maritime Museum of San Diego.)

houses in the early 1900s with a hastiness attested to today by the crooked angles of the windowsills as the landfill continues to settle.

Although many of the buildings are still being restored, the renovation of those along Fulton Street (its name is taken from Robert Fulton, who once docked his famous steamboat here) is complete. The first building of the Fulton Fish Market was constructed by the city in 1869; today's building at the water's edge has been in use since 1907. The adjacent Fulton Market is the third market building to stand on its site since 1822. Originally occupied by butchers, it now offers three stories of shops and specialty restaurants.

Across Fulton Street from the market is Schermerhorn Row, a row of early nineteenth-century buildings housing more shops and restaurants. Information on the seaport area is available at the Visitor's Center at 12 Fulton Street and the Pier 16 ticket booth. Abundant parking is available in the historic district.

Museum ships are docked at the foot of Fulton Street at Piers 15 and 16. Vessels that may be boarded include the *Peking,* a 347-foot four-masted bark built in 1911; the *Wavertree,* a 293-foot full-rigged ship built in 1885; the schooner *Pioneer,* built in 1885; the original *Ambrose* Lightship; and others.

Seaport Experience Theater, in the Trans-Lux Seaport Theater at 210 Front Street, is a multimedia presentation that deals with the past and present seaport. The computerized environmental theater program uses more than 30 screens, 100 projectors, and many special effects, including sea spray, fog, fire, lightning, and thunder.

Activities

Demonstration squad on ships and piers during summer months, ship restorations and gallery exhibitions, craft demonstrations, guided tours, lectures, films, summer concerts and sailing on the schooner *Pioneer,* and excursions on Seaport Line vessels.

Admission

Entry fee and theater admission. Memberships are available. Museum ships are open daily, 10 A.M.–5 P.M., year-round. Closed Thanksgiving, Christmas, and New Year's Day. The Seaport Experience Theater presents shows hourly, Sunday–Thursday, 11 A.M.–6:30 P.M., Fridays and Saturdays, 11 A.M.–8 P.M.

PORT JEFFERSON

Historical Society of Greater Port Jefferson

Historical Society of Greater Port Jefferson
115 Prospect Street
P.O. Box 586
Port Jefferson, NY 11777
(516) 473-2665

Location
From New York City take I-495 east sixty-four miles to exit for SR-112. Follow it north six miles to SR-25A, heading west to Port Jefferson on the north shore of Long Island (just eighteen miles south of Bridgeport, Connecticut, across Long Island Sound).

Highlights
Maritime history of the region

General Information
The Historical Society of Greater Port Jefferson maintains a small maritime museum with general artifacts and displays.

Admission
Call the society for information about their opening hours.

SAG HARBOR
Sag Harbor Whaling Museum

Sag Harbor Whaling Museum
Main Street
P.O. Box 1327
Sag Harbor, NY 11963
(516) 725-0770

Location
On Long Island take SR-24 eleven miles to SR-27. Head east fifteen miles to Bridgehampton, then turn north on SR-114 five miles to Sag Harbor. The museum is opposite the library.

Highlights
Whaleboat
Whale tryworks, tools, and artifacts
Ship models
Scrimshaw
Nautical gift shop

General Information
Sag Harbor Whaling Museum, founded in 1936, is housed in a building that was erected in 1895 as a home for Benjamin Hunting, an owner of whale ships. As you approach the building you will see the beautiful Corinthian columns. A whaleboat is outside at the left of the museum. At the right in front of the museum are the tryworks—three large kettles used on board whale boats for boiling the blubber to render whale oil.

As you enter the museum you will pass through the genuine jaw bones of a right whale. These were brought back to Sag Harbor by a whaler and have been on display for almost 100 years.

Exhibits feature whaling equipment, scrimshaw, oil paintings, ship models, fishing equipment, logbooks, and other colonial pieces connected with eastern Long Island.

Admission
Entry fee. Open daily, 1 P.M.–5 P.M., 15 May–20 September.

SOUTHOLD

Southold Historical Society and Lighthouse Marine Museum

Southold Historical Society and Marine Museum
Main Road and Maple Lane
Box 1
Southold, NY 11971
(516) 765-5500

Location
On Long Island follow I-495 approximately seventy-five miles to Riverhead. Bear northeast on SR-25 the twenty-three miles to Southold. The museum is at Horton's Point off SR-25.

Highlights
Lighthouse

General Information
Southold Historical Society and Lighthouse Marine Museum was established to preserve artifacts, paintings, logs, and letters of

maritime interest and an 1857 lighthouse. Horton's Point was selected as a site for a lighthouse because it rises 110 feet above the high-tide line. Thus, it provided navigational aid in an area characterized by many shipwrecks. The museum now houses exhibits of marine and nautical objects, paintings, and documents.

Admission
Entry fee. Open Saturdays and Sundays only, 1 P.M.–5 P.M., July and August.

WEST SAYVILLE
Suffolk Marine Museum

Suffolk Marine Museum
Montauk Highway
P.O. Box 144
West Sayville, NY 11796
(516) 567-1733

Location
West Sayville is on the south-central shore of Long Island. From New York City take I-495 forty-nine miles to the junction of SR-27. Follow that east ten miles to West Sayville. The museum is on the grounds of the West Sayville Golf Course.

Highlights
The *Priscilla* (oyster vessel)
The *Modesty* (oyster sloop)
The *Charlotte* (1880s tugboat)
Ship models
The Dolphin (newspaper)
Library

General Information
Suffolk Marine Museum, founded in 1966, features ship models, paintings, and artifacts. Collections include: maritime history; a significant small-craft collection in excess of fifty vessels ranging in size from nine-foot gunning punts to the sixty-five-foot *Priscilla,* an 1888 oyster vessel; lifesaving equipment; shipwreck artifacts;

Penney Boatshop; Rudolph Oyster House; and the historic ships *Modesty,* a 1923 oyster sloop, and *Charlotte,* an 1880s tugboat.

A library of books, documents, photographs, press clippings, and periodicals relating to maritime history is available to researchers by appointment.

Activities
Lectures, slide shows, oral history, and folkcraft demonstrations

Admission
No entry fee, but donations accepted. Open Monday–Saturday, 10 A.M.–3 P.M., Sunday, noon–4 P.M., year-round. Closed Thanksgiving, Christmas, New Year's Day, Easter, and Election Day.

NEW JERSEY

ATLANTIC CITY
Historic Gardner's Basin

Historic Gardner's Basin
North New Hampshire Avenue and the Bay
Atlantic City, NJ 08401
(609) 348-2880

Location
The basin is situated at the northeast end of Atlantic City on North New Hampshire Avenue.

Highlights
The *Young American* (tall ship)
Twenty-five vessels
Aquarium

General Information
Historic Gardner's Basin, founded in 1976, is a maritime village within the Atlantic City waterfront homes that predate 1900. The site is where the city was founded and was both the center of South Jersey's fishing industry and the hub of rumrunning.

Collections include twenty-five vessels, some of which are the oldest or the last of their kind in the nation or the world. The visitor will find maritime artifacts and seafaring memorabilia; working and living exhibits on lobstermen; and sculpture, paintings, and working and living exhibits of the clammer (clam digger).

Activities
Guided tours, lectures, films, gallery talks, concerts, arts festivals, educational programs, a three-hour sail on the *Young America* (the only American-constructed square-rigger sailing with passengers in the world today).

Admission
No entry fee. Memberships are available. Open daily, 9:30 A.M.–5:30 P.M., year-round. Closed Christmas and New Year's Day.

BARNEGAT LIGHT
Barnegat Lighthouse

Barnegat Lighthouse
Division of Parks and Forestry
State Park Service CN 404
P.O. Box 167
Barnegat Light, NJ 08006
(609) 494-2016

Location
Barnegat Light lies twenty-five miles north of Atlantic City on the northern tip of Long Beach Island in Ocean County. It can be

reached from Garden State Parkway by exiting onto Rte. 72 (exit 63) to North Long Beach Island Boulevard.

Highlights
Barnegat Lighthouse

General Information
This "Grand Old Champion of the Tides" is a great piece of American sculpture, with the power to move minds and seize hearts. The first lighthouse on record was built in Barnegat Inlet, Barnegat City, in 1834. It cost $6,000, which was appropriated by Congress on 30 June 1834 for that purpose. The tower, fifty feet high, was built of brick and whitewashed from top to bottom. The light, which was the fourth placed on the coast of New Jersey, was white and "fixed" and did not flash. All of the exposed metal parts were painted a dead black, and whale oil was used for the illuminant.

The original structure fell into the water in the early part of 1856. At that time a temporary wooden tower was hastily constructed farther inland and lighted with lamps salvaged from the wreck of the old one. General George G. Meade had Barnegat reconstructed in 1857–58.

The lighthouse rises 172 feet above the tides that mark Barnegat Shoals, the scene of more than 200 shipwrecks. An excellent view is available from the base. The great Fresnel lens was dismantled and stored in the Tomkinsville Lighthouse Depot on Staten Island for possible reuse and future service. When the town of Barnegat Light established a museum of local history in 1954, the lens was returned and is now on display.

Activities
Visitors are invited to enjoy the lighthouse and the coastal panorama from the lightkeeper's catwalk.

Admission
Entry fee. Open Saturdays and Sundays, 2 P.M.–5 P.M., June and September; daily, 2 P.M.–5 P.M., July and August.

HACKENSACK
U.S. Naval Museum/Submarine USS *Ling*

Submarine Memorial Association
150 River Street
P.O. Box 395
Hackensack, NJ 07601
(201) 342-3268

Location
The USS *Ling* is docked at the corner of River and Court Streets in Hackensack, five miles west of the George Washington Bridge (I-80) at Borg Park.

Highlights
The USS *Ling* (SS-297) (submarine)

General Information
The U.S. Naval Museum/Submarine USS *Ling* Memorial Association was founded in 1973 as a memorial to those who served

The USS *Ling* (SS 297), partially built at the Cramp Yard in Philadelphia, was one of the few fleet boats completed by the Boston Navy Yard. The *Ling* arrived in the Pacific to make one Atlantic patrol before the termination of World War II. The 312-foot-long submarine was decommissioned on 16 October 1946 and later served as a training vessel. The *Ling* arrived at its berth at the U.S. Naval Museum Submarine Memorial at Borg Park on the shore of the Hackensack River in Hackensack, New Jersey, on 13 January 1973.

aboard submarines during World War II. The *Ling* was built by the Cramp Shipbuilding Company in Philadelphia and outfitted in the Boston Navy Yard. She was commissioned 8 June 1945, and on 13 January 1973 the Submarine Memorial Association brought her to Borg Park in Hackensack.

Activities
Guided tours of the vessel

Admission
Entry fee. Open daily, 10 A.M.–4 P.M., year-round.

HIGHLANDS
Sandy Hook Museum

Sandy Hook Museum
c/o Twin Lights Historic Site
P.O. Box 437
Highlands, NJ 07732
(201) 872-0115

Location
To reach Highlands take the Garden State Parkway to Keyport. Exit onto SR-36, heading east the thirteen miles to Highlands. The museum is located in Gateway National Recreation Area, one block west of the Sandy Hook Lighthouse on a long spit of sand extending north from the New Jersey shore.

Highlights
Gift shop

General Information
Sandy Hook Museum, founded in 1968, is in the old guard house at Fort Hancock and is operated by the National Park Service. The Sandy Hook Lighthouse is the oldest operating lighthouse in America (1764). Even though the museum contains a limited number of maritime exhibits, the Gateway National Recreation Area is worth visiting because of the additional museums it offers, including the Museum at Navesink Lighthouses, a part of the Twin Lights Historic Site.

Admission
No entry fee. Open daily, 1 P.M.–5 P.M., Memorial Day–Labor Day; Saturdays and Sundays, 1 P.M.–5 P.M., the rest of the year.

Twin Lights State Historic Site

Twin Lights State Historic Site
Lighthouse Road
Highlands, NJ 07732
(201) 872-1814

Location
To reach Highlands take the Garden State Parkway to Keyport. Exit onto SR-36 heading east the thirteen miles to Highlands. The Historic Site is on the grounds of the Gateway National Recreation Area.

Highlights
The Twin Lights
Gift shop

General Information
Twin Lights has served as a beacon for ships since 1828, having been rebuilt in 1862 during Lincoln's term as president. Today, a state-maintained occulting white light is seen from the north tower. The original lighthouse, which houses the nautical and lifesaving museum, is a brownstone structure with towers at both ends.

From Sandy Hook to Cape May, five major lighthouses marked New Jersey's 144-mile Atlantic coastline. Sandy Hook, Navesink (Twin Lights), Barnegat, Absecon, and Cape May lighthouses all had powerful lenses, the beacons of which could be seen eighteen to twenty miles from the shore. The most powerful beacon was installed at the Navesink Light Station (Twin Lights) in 1898. Marking the westerly side of the entrance to New York Harbor, the twenty-five-million-candlepower beam was the brightest in the country and could be seen twenty-two miles away.

Activities
Audio stations assist in recounting the site's history. The public may climb sixty-four steps to an observation deck at the top of the north tower.

Admission
No entry fee, but donations accepted. Open daily, 9 A.M.–5 P.M., year-round. Closed Thanksgiving, Christmas, and New Year's Day.

HOBOKEN

Hudson Waterfront Museum

The Hudson Waterfront Museum
P.O. Box 1602
West New York, NJ 07093
(201) 420-1789 or 662-1229

Location
The museum is located at the foot of Newark Street at Hoboken's Erie Lackawanna Plaza, immediately north of the Hoboken PATH (subway) Terminal.

Highlights
The *Philip T. Feeney* (1898 tugboat)
Lehigh Valley Railroad Barge 79
Library/archives
Gift shop

General Information
Hudson Waterfront Museum was established in 1989 as a local focus for the appreciation of the region's waterfront heritage, including the people, shipping, and railroads of the area. Through a series of floating, pier-side, and land-based spaces, the museum can serve local families, school groups, tourists, and people whose livelihoods have been tied to waterfront-related industries. The museum depicts the work, life, and transportation along the Hud-

son during its commercial heyday. On display are the 1892 *Phillip T. Feeney* tugboat and the 1914 Lehigh Valley Railroad Barge 79. Aboard the 79 is the museum's permanent collection of *Erie Railroad* magazine photos (1943–52), a "riptide" dingy, hawsers, tools, tugboat fenders, and much more.

Handcrafted wooden vessels of American origin were once nestled along the shores of the Port of New York. Prior to tunnel and bridge construction, cargo had to be transported by water across the Hudson River. To perform this function, various railroad companies maintained large fleets of barges and tugs. This "Lighterage System" used many types of craft including scows, hold barges, sticklighters, car floats, and covered barges. There were also excursion barges, emigrant barges, produce barges, ice barges, livestock barges, and steel-covered barges. The museum provides information on all of this historical past.

Activities
Try your hand with a heaving line, throwing the eye of the line, and making up a Flemish coil. See a continuous video display titled "Tales of the Waterfront," and attend informational lectures.

Admission
No entry fee. Memberships are available. Open Thursdays, 4 P.M.–8 P.M., and Sundays, 1 P.M.–5 P.M., year-round.

KEYPORT
Steamboat Dock Museum

Steamboat Dock Museum
P.O. Box 312
Keyport, NJ 07735
(201) 739-6390

Location
Keyport sits on the Raritan Bay about ten miles southeast of Sayreville. The museum is located on American Legion Drive in the center of town, just at the foot of Broad Street.

Highlights
Model of the *Keyport* (steamboat)
Oystering displays and photos
Aeromarine displays and photos

General Information
The Steamboat Dock Museum, founded in 1974, contains much of the history of the Kearney family, who settled in the area in 1714. A major shipping industry began in 1830, and the town grew and prospered. The Chingarora oyster, harvested from the Raritan Bay, became world famous. In the mid-1800s, not long after Fulton's first steamboat, Benjamin Terry, a builder and entrepreneur, began his steamboat industry, launching more steamboats from the Keyport shores than competitors in Jersey City and Camden.

Admission
No entry fee. Open Sundays, 1 P.M.–4 P.M., late June–September.

PINE BEACH
Farragut Marine Museum

Farragut Marine Museum
Admiral Farragut Academy
Riverside Drive
Pine Beach, NJ 08741
(201) 349-4406/0957

Location
Follow the Garden State Parkway to Toms River. The museum is in Russell Hall (formerly Farragut Hall) on the campus of the Admiral Farragut Academy on Toms River at Pine Beach.

Highlights
Replica of Farragut's cabin in the USS *Hartford*
Periscope from German U-Boat sunk by the USS *Roper* (DD-147) in 1942

General Information
Farragut Marine Museum, founded in 1956, was established to inspire the cadets of Farragut Academy and to instill in them a patriotic pride in the past greatness of our nation as they prepare for their careers.

The museum has acquired artifacts, letters, books, and paintings of the maritime and military heritage of the United States. Collections include acquisition of such items as Admiral David A. Farragut's Bible and telescope as well as the periscope from the German U-boat sunk by the USS *Roper* (DD-147) in 1942.

Activities
Group tours available

Admission
No entry fee. Open Monday–Friday, 9 A.M.–5 P.M., year-round. Group tours are available by appointment on weekends throughout the year.

PENNSYLVANIA (EASTERN)

EASTON
Canal Museum and Hugh Moore Park

Canal Museum and Hugh Moore Park
200 South Delaware Drive
P.O. Box 877
Easton, PA 18044-0877
(215) 250-6700

Location
Easton is on the Delaware River, fifteen miles east of Allentown via I-78. Once in town, follow the brown "Canal Boat" signs to the park.

Highlights
Canal Museum
Lock Tender's House Museum
Mule-drawn canal boat
Lehigh Canal
Picnic areas and playgrounds
The Lock Tender (newsletter)
Library (10,000 volumes)
Bookstore

General Information
The Canal Museum, founded in 1970, is housed in a canal-era building on the site of one of the most active of America's nineteenth-century canal ports. The museum tells the story of our country's great towpath canal era though maintaining archives and actively searching for materials that are in danger of being lost. It maintains manuscript collections, photo archives, and a 10,000-volume library on canals of the towpath era and related industries.

Hugh Moore Park conserves history and nature in exceptional unison. It includes six miles of the Lehigh Canal, a restored Lock Tender's House Museum, three restored canal locks, the Chain Dam, a mule-drawn canal boat ride, and the Glendon and Abbott Street Industrial Ruins. The park also provides bike paths, hiking trails, picnic areas, pavilions, playgrounds, and bicycle, canoe, and pedal boat rentals.

Activities
Guided tours, lectures, films, hiking trails, boat and bike rentals, mule-drawn canal boat rides, annual Canal Festival, annual Canal History and Technology Symposium

Admission
Entry fee. Memberships are available. Open Monday–Saturday, 10 A.M.–4 P.M., Sunday, 1 P.M.–5 P.M., year-round. Closed Thanksgiving, Christmas, and New Year's Day.

PHILADELPHIA

Cigna Museum and Art Collection

Cigna Museum and Art Collection
1600 Arch Street
Philadelphia, PA 19103
(215) 523-4894

Location
The museum is located at 1600 Arch Street in downtown Philadelphia.

Highlights
Ship models
Marine paintings (American and British)

General Information
Founded in 1925, Cigna Museum exhibits a collection of eighteenth- and nineteenth-century marine and fire-fighting objects and eighteenth- to twentieth-century American fine art. Included are paintings, models, prints, equipment, and manuscripts.

Activities
Permanent and changing exhibits, guided tours by appointment, and loan exhibits

Admission
No entry fee. Open Monday–Friday, 9 A.M.–5 P.M., year-round. Closed national holidays.

Franklin Institute

Franklin Institute
20th Street and Benjamin Franklin Parkway
Philadelphia, PA 19103
(215) 448-1200

Location
The institute sits one-half mile northwest of Center City Philadelphia off the Ben Franklin Parkway.

Highlights
Shipbuilding on the Delaware River
Ship models
Gift shop

General Information
The Franklin Institute was established in 1934 as a science and technology museum. As such, it maintains an exhibit on shipbuilding on the Delaware River that consists particularly of shipyards from their inception (when Philadelphia was founded) until the early 1980s, or, in other words, from wooden ships to "iron" ones.

Displays of ship models include the Russian *Variag,* a tow-tank used for ship hull research, an exhibit about John Lenthall, an early naval architect, and a model of the *Cuba* (the original is in the Smithsonian in Washington, D.C.).

Archives hold paintings, logbooks, glass photography plates, photographs, apprentice books, etc.

Activities
Audiovisual programs on shipbuilding during World War II

Admission
Entry fee. Open daily, 10 A.M.–5 P.M., year-round. Closed Thanksgiving, Christmas, and New Year's Day.

Penn's Landing
(*see also:* Philadelphia Maritime Museum)

Penn's Landing
P.O. Box 928
Philadelphia, PA 19105
(215) 923-8181

Location
The landing, the location of a number of boardable historical ships, is between Market and Lombard Streets. Here, on the Delaware River waterfront, William Penn landed in 1682.

Highlights
The USS *Becuna* (submarine)
The USS *Olympia*
Boardable historic ships

General Information
The *Barnegat* Lightship, built in 1904, lit the shipping lanes of the Port of Philadelphia for sixty-three years.

The barkentine *Gasela* (1883), Philadelphia's 103-year-old museum ship, was built in Portugal. According to Portuguese tradition, her planking is "stone pine" cut from forests planted by Prince Henry the Navigator of the fifteenth century. Whether or not this is true, the wood is still resinous and solid after 103 years. Little is known of her very early history. From the turn of the century until 1962, however, she earned her living on the Grand Banks, fishing for cod from dories. In that year a wealthy Philadelphian bought her and presented her to the Philadelphia Maritime Museum. She is now owned by Penn's Landing Corporation and is under the management of the Philadelphia Ship Preservation Guild.

The USS *Becuna* is a *Guppy*-class submarine. She was commissioned in 1944 to serve in Admiral William Halsey's Seventh Fleet in the South Pacific.

The USS *Olympia,* Admiral Dewey's flagship during the Spanish-American War, brought back the body of the Unknown Solder in 1921.

Admission
The *Barnegat:* Entry fee. Open daily, 11 A.M.–4 P.M., Memorial Day–Labor Day; Saturdays and Sundays only, noon–5 P.M., the rest of the year. Closed Christmas and New Year's Day.

The *Gasela:* Admission included in the *Barnegat* fee. Open the same hours as the *Barnegat*.

The *Becuna:* Entry fee. Open daily, 10 A.M.–4:30 P.M., Memorial Day–Labor Day; 10 A.M.–4 P.M., the rest of the year. Closed Christmas and New Year's Day.

The *Olympia:* Admission included in the *Becuna* fee. Open the same hours as the *Becuna.*

Philadelphia Maritime Museum
(*See also:* Penn's Landing)

Philadelphia Maritime Museum
321 Chestnut Street
Philadelphia, PA 19106
(215) 925-5439

Location
In downtown Philadelphia, go five blocks west of the Delaware River on Chestnut Street. The museum is one block south of Market Street across from the Independence National Historical Park.

Highlights
Ship models
Navigational instruments
Boatbuilding
Workshop on the water
Library

General Information
Philadelphia Maritime Museum, founded in 1961, preserves the maritime heritage of the Delaware River and Bay. For over three hundred years Philadelphia has been a major port city. Its adjacent waterways, particularly the Delaware and Schuylkill rivers, have been a vital part of the city's economic life since William Penn founded his "Greate Towne" in 1682. Here the U.S. Navy was founded in 1775, the first steamboat was built, and the first atomic-powered vessel was launched.

Marine art, ship models, early navigational instruments, shipbuilding tools, and weapons vividly portray the mariner's world. The museum is a treasure house of maritime lore found in manuscripts, rare books, and historic photographs, maps, and charts. The museum is the repository of the Titanic Historical Society's collection; an exhibition titled "The *Titanic* and Her Era" offers insights into this famed vessel.

The museum's workshop on the water at Penn's Landing on the Delaware River is not only an active boatbuilding shop, it also houses exhibits of small pleasure and working boats of the Delaware River and Bay, thus preserving a way of life on the river that is fast disappearing.

A library is open to the public by appointment.

Activities
Guided tours, lectures, films, boat conservation, boatbuilding classes.

Admission
No entry fee, but donations accepted. Memberships are available. Open Monday–Saturday, 10 A.M.–5 P.M., Sunday, 1 P.M.–5 P.M., year-round. Closed Thanksgiving, 24, 25, and 31 December, New Year's Day, and Easter.

DELAWARE

BOWERS
Bowers Beach Maritime Museum

Bowers Beach Maritime Museum, Inc.
Cooper Avenue
Frederica, DE 19946
(302) 335-3462

Location
Bowers is off Rte. 113, ten miles southeast of Dover. Take the Little Heaven exit east toward the beach.

Highlights
Maritime history

General Information
Bowers Beach Maritime Museum was founded in 1976. It is located on the site of a small colonial fishing village and features paintings and drawings (watercolor, pen and ink). Artifacts from old two-masted schooners and passenger and freight boats are on display.

Activities
Guided tours, lectures, and a training ground for professional museum workers

Admission
No entry fee. Memberships are available. Open Saturdays, Sundays, and holidays, 1 P.M.–4 P.M., in the summer; by appointment only in the winter.

LEWES
Cannon Ball Marine Museum

Cannon Ball Marine Museum
Attn: Henry P. Marshall
119 West 3rd Street
Lewes, DE 19958
(302) 645-8740

Location
Lewes is on Rte. 9, thirty miles southeast of Dover near the Atlantic coastline.

Highlights
The *Overfalls* (lightship)
U.S. Coast Guard boathouse
Newsletter

General Information
Cannon Ball Marine Museum, founded in 1972, is housed in Cannon Ball House, noted for having been hit by a cannonball in the War of 1812. The Lewes Historical Society has been restoring seven historical homes in Lewes including the Cannon Ball House, which now houses maritime exhibits of ship models and a "Pilot Room" devoted to artifacts and items about the ship pilots of the area. The lightship *Overfalls* is a part of the museum and is located on the canal on Ship Carpenter Street.

Activities
Lectures, films, annual craft fair, annual flea market, and seminars

Admission
Entry fee. Open Tuesdays, Thursdays, and Saturdays, 10 A.M.–3 P.M., June–September.

WILMINGTON
USCGC *Mohawk*

Mohawk, Inc.
901 Washington Street
Wilmington, DE 19801
(302) 658-8760

Location
The USCGC *Mohawk* is located off I-95 at the foot of King Street on the Christina River. She is moored next to Wilmington's restored Victorian era railroad station.

Highlights
The *Mohawk* (U.S. Coast Guard cutter)

General Information
The cutter *Mohawk,* launched in Wilmington in 1934, was established in 1983 as a museum and memorial dedicated to all coast guard, navy, and merchant marine seamen who served in the Battle of the Atlantic during World War II. Retrofitted with her 1943 colors, the *Mohawk* is the only known operational memorial

to the Battle of the Atlantic. One can go on board and see, hear, touch, and smell life at sea during that heroic period. (A cruising memorial that visits East Coast ports, she has also been a proud escort of the *Queen Elizabeth II,* the SS *Norway,* and other festive arrivals of international ships.)

Activities
With galley and heads, the *Mohawk* can accommodate 300 in port for conferences and parties (quarters for the all-volunteer crew sleep over 50).

Admission
No entry fee, but donations accepted. Open Saturdays, 9 A.M.–3 P.M., summers only.

MARYLAND

ANNAPOLIS
Historic Annapolis

Historic Annapolis, Inc.
77 Main Street or 194 Prince George
Annapolis, MD 21401
(301) 267-8149/7619
(Maritime Museum: 268-5576)

Location
Annapolis sits on the Chesapeake Bay thirty-two miles east of Washington, D.C., off Rte. 50.

Highlights
The general historical past of Annapolis
The William Paca House
Tobacco Prise House
Victualling Warehouse Maritime Museum

General Information
Collections include: architecture and decorative arts; Hancock's Resolution; the historic (1765) William Paca House and Garden; Old Treasury Building; Tobacco Prise House; barracks; and the Victualling Warehouse Maritime Museum. The latter features a diorama of the Annapolis waterfront circa 1751–91, when Annapolis was the principal seaport of the upper Chesapeake Bay. Also exhibited are shipbuilding tools, half-woven sails, military clothes, oak barrels, wine bottles, and other displays.

Activities
Guided tours, lectures, films, educational programs, research programs, and special events

Admission
Entry fee. Contact the office for the opening hours of the various historic buildings. The maritime museum is open daily, 11 A.M.–4:30 P.M., year-round.

U.S. Naval Academy Museum

U.S. Naval Academy Museum
U.S. Naval Academy
Annapolis, MD 21402
(301) 267-2108/2109

Location
Annapolis sits on the Chesapeake Bay, thirty-two miles east of Washington, D.C., off Rte. 50.

Highlights
John Paul Jones crypt
Ship models
Library

General Information
The U.S. Naval Academy Museum, located in Preble Hall, was founded in 1845. It contains two galleries of indoor historical exhibits. Many other buildings on the Naval Academy grounds also exhibit items from the collection. A large display can be found in the crypt of John Paul Jones, located in the Naval Academy Chapel.

The museum serves as an educational and inspirational resource for the brigade of midshipmen at the Academy as well as for all of us. Utilizing three-dimensional and graphic materials, the museum demonstrates the navy's role in war and in peace.

The museum originated in 1845 with the Naval Academy Lyceum, a collection of historic and natural objects, scientific models and apparatus, and works of art brought together for study and discussion. In 1888 the U.S. Naval Lyceum at the New York Navy Yard was disbanded, and its large collection of objects was transferred to the Naval Academy.

The museum's holdings include ship models, paintings, prints, flags, uniforms, weapons, medals, sculpture, manuscripts, rare books, photographs, ships' instruments and gear, and a wide variety of personal memorabilia and natural objects.

A library contains books on U.S. Navy and Naval Academy history, marine architecture, naval flags, and marine art.

Activities
Guided tours, hobby workshops, and educational programs

Admission
No entry fee. Open Monday–Saturday, 9 A.M.–5 P.M., Sunday, 11 A.M.–5 P.M., year-round. Closed Thanksgiving, Christmas, and New Year's Day.

BALTIMORE
Baltimore Maritime Museum

Baltimore Maritime Museum
Pier 4, Pratt Street
Baltimore, MD 21202
(301) 396-3854

Location
The Baltimore Maritime Museum is in Baltimore's Inner Harbor.

Highlights
The *Chesapeake* (lightship)
The USS *Torsk* (submarine)

General Information
The Baltimore Maritime Museum offers guided tours through the USS *Torsk,* the last U.S. submarine to sink enemy shipping in World War II. Across the pier is the lightship *Cheasapeake,* a floating lighthouse designed to aid shipping in the Chesapeake Bay.

The U.S. Coast Guard cutter *Taney* will be exhibited soon. She was the last ship afloat after the Japanese attack on Pearl Harbor.

Admission
Entry fee. Open daily, 9:30 A.M.–7 P.M. while daylight savings time is in effect; 9:30 A.M.–4:30 P.M. the rest of the year.

Baltimore Museum of Industry

Baltimore Museum of Industry
1415 Key Highway
Baltimore, MD 21230
(301) 727-4808

Location
Exit off I-395 onto Montgomery Street, then head south toward Ft. McHenry. The museum is near the steam tug *Baltimore,* which is docked on the south side of the old Baltimore harbor on Key Highway.

Highlights
The *Baltimore* (steam tug)
Library

General Information
The Baltimore Museum of Industry, founded in 1981, is housed in an oyster cannery. A wide variety of industry-related exhibits are displayed and machinery is demonstrated.

Activities
Tour of the steam tug *Baltimore* (by appointment)

Admission
Entry fee. Open Tuesday–Sunday, noon–5 P.M., year-round.

U.S. Frigate *Constellation*

U.S. Frigate *Constellation*
Inner Harbor
Pier 1, Pratt Street
Baltimore, MD 21202
(301) 539-1797

Location
Constellation Dock is located at the intersection of Pratt and Light Streets in Baltimore's Inner Harbor.

Highlights
The U.S. Frigate *Constellation*

General Information
Now a museum, founded in 1955, the U.S. Frigate *Constellation* is a working restoration of the first of six frigates designed and built for the U.S. Navy. Visitors will feel her history and relive her glory as they explore the decks of the first commissioned ship of the U.S. Navy, launched 7 September 1797. The first of our fledgling navy to put to sea, the *Constellation* was also the first to engage and the first to defeat a man-of-war from the old world, namely, the French frigate *l'Insurgente* in 1799. She was also used against pirates in Tripoli in 1802 and the British in 1812, and she saw action in the Civil War and as an auxiliary flagship of the Atlantic Fleet in World War II.

Activities
Guided tours

Admission
Entry fee. Open daily, 10 A.M.–8 P.M., 15 June–Labor Day; 10 A.M.–6 P.M., after Labor Day–14 October; 10 A.M.–4 P.M., the rest of the year. Closed 24, 25, and 31 December and New Year's Day.

Radcliffe Maritime Museum

Radcliffe Maritime Museum
Maryland Historical Society
201 West Monument Street
Baltimore, MD 21201
(301) 685-3750

Location
The museum is located one mile north of downtown Baltimore.

Highlights
Ship models

General Information
The Radcliffe Maritime Museum exhibits rigged ship models, decorative carvings, and items that illustrate Maryland's maritime heritage.

Admission
No entry fee. Open Tuesday–Saturday, 11 A.M.–4 P.M., Sunday, 1 P.M.–5 P.M., year-round. (Summer hours are subject to change.)

Steamship Historical Society of America Collection

Steamship Historical Society of America Collection
1420 Maryland Avenue
University of Baltimore Library
Baltimore, MD 21201
(301) 625-3134

Location
The collection is housed at the University of Baltimore Library, north of Baltimore's downtown area on Maryland Avenue.

Highlights
Library (4,700 volumes)

General Information
The Steamship Historical Society of America Collection was founded in 1940 and maintains one of the largest libraries in North America devoted exclusively to steamboat and steamship history. This professionally staffed facility is within easy walking distance of Pennsylvania Station.

The library contains books, reports, pamphlets, 100,000 photographs in the field of powered shipping and navigation, 25,000 postcards, microfilm and microfiche readers, and slide-viewing equipment.

Activities
Marine research in person and by mail

Admission
No entry fee. Open for research Monday–Friday, 8 A.M.–4 P.M. (Inquire for current schedule of Saturday opening hours.)

CAMBRIDGE
Brannock Maritime Museum

Brannock Maritime Museum
210 Talbot Street
Cambridge, MD 21613
(301) 228-6938

Location
Cambridge, on Maryland's Eastern Shore, is just off Rte. 50 at the Choptank River. It is Maryland's second largest deepwater port.

Highlights
Whaling and shipbuilding history

General Information
Brannock Maritime Museum contains exhibits of whaling ships and navigational instruments that date back to the 1700s. A small, privately funded museum, it features shipbuilding and memorabilia strictly from this part of the Chesapeake Bay.

Admission
No entry fee. Call or write the museum for information about their opening hours.

Dorchester Heritage Museum

Dorchester Heritage Museum
Rte. 1, Box 329
Horn Point
Cambridge, MD 21613
(301) 228-6172

Location
Cambridge is located on Maryland's Eastern Shore, approximately forty-five miles south of the Chesapeake Bay Bridge on Rte. 50.

Highlights
Last Eastern Shore gunning boat

General Information
Dorchester Heritage Museum, founded in 1684, contains maritime, aircraft, farming, and Indian exhibits in a working museum. Exhibits include one of the last Eastern Shore gunning boats used by legal and illegal market hunters.

Activities
An annual antique aircraft fly-in the weekend before Memorial Day

Admission
No entry fee. Open Saturdays and Sundays only, 1 P.M.–4:30 P.M., 15 April–30 October.

CHESAPEAKE CITY

C and D Canal Museum

(Also known as the Chesapeake and Delaware Canal Museum)

C and D Canal Museum
Chesapeake City, MD 21915
(301) 885-5621

Location

Chesapeake City is on the west end of the canal that links the Delaware and Elk Rivers. The most direct route from Maryland is to take the Elkton exit off I-95 north/south, then follow back roads southeast the few miles to Chesapeake City.

Highlights

Old Lock Pump House
Working model of a waterwheel and lock
Steam engines

General Information

Housed in the original canal/pump house complex, the museum includes a working model of a waterwheel and lock, paintings, maps, documents, and artifacts pertaining to the history of this waterway.

The Old Lock Pump House, built over a century ago, contained a steam engine, boilers, and pumps to replace water lost in opening and closing a nearby canal lock. The U.S. Army Corps of Engineers has carefully preserved the pump complex since it went out of use in 1926.

Admission

No entry fee. Open Monday–Saturday, 8 A.M.–4:30 P.M., Sunday, 10 A.M.–6 P.M., Easter–31 October. Closed Sundays and holidays the rest of the year.

COLTONS POINT

St. Clements Island–Potomac River Museum

St. Clements Island–Potomac River Museum
General Delivery
Coltons Point, MD 20626
(301) 769-2222

Location
Take Rte. 301 forty miles south of Washington, D.C., exiting onto SR-234. Head east the twelve miles to Chaptico, then take SR-238 south the eleven miles to Coltons Point. Twenty-five miles upstream from the Chesapeake Bay on the Potomac River, Coltons Point is accessible by water or land.

Highlights
Boat tour to St. Clement's Island
Finer Points (newsletter)
Library
Gift shop

General Information
St. Clements Island–Potomac River Museum, founded in 1975, has been established to tell the story of the region, the island, and the people that have inhabited the bank of the Potomac River.

In 1634 a group of adventurers traveled from their homes in England in pursuit of a new land in which they would be free from oppression. On 25 March the *Ark* and the *Dove* dropped anchor on a small island in the Potomac River where their passengers, who were to become Maryland's first settlers, stopped and prayed for their safety and success. That place is now known as St. Clement's Island, a landmark in the history of Maryland.

Activities
Self-guided tours, picnic areas, public dock, a slide presentation, a children's workshop, and a library

Admission
No entry fee for the museum, but a modest fee for the boat trip to St. Clements Island. Open Monday–Friday, 9 A.M.–5 P.M., Saturdays and Sundays only, noon–5 P.M., Memorial Day–Labor Day.

CRISFIELD

Governor J. Millard Tawes Historical Museum

Governor J. Millard Tawes Historical Museum
Somers Cove
P.O. Box 253
Crisfield, MD 21817
(301) 968-2501

Location
Crisfield is on the southernmost point of Maryland's Eastern Shore, approached via SR-413 south out of Salisbury.

Highlights
Artwork, folk art, maritime, and local history
Seafood industry

General Information
Governor J. Millard Tawes Museum, founded in 1982, exhibits a collection of photographs, paintings, and memorabilia from the life of this late Crisfield resident and former Maryland governor. There are also exhibits relating to the history of Crisfield and the seafood industry

Admission
Entry fee. Open daily, 10 A.M.–4 P.M., year-round.

HAVRE DE GRACE

Susquehanna Museum

Susquehanna Museum of Havre de Grace
P.O. Box 253
Havre de Grace, MD 21078
(301) 939-5780

Location
Off I-95 north/south take the exit at SR-155. Havre de Grace lies at the mouth of the Susquehanna River, the southern terminal of the Susquehanna and Tidewater Canal that empties into the upper Chesapeake Bay.

Highlights
Restored lock house

General Information
The Susquehanna Museum, founded in 1970, is committed to preserving the history of Havre de Grace. The museum building is the restored lock house, which was built in 1840 and is furnished in keeping with the mid-1800s.

In addition to the restored house, the pilot bridge over the lock has been restored, and work has started on restoring the lock. The state will be dredging the boat basin to convert it into a shad breeding pond.

In the forty-five mile run to the canal's northern terminal at Wrightsville, Pennsylvania, the mule-drawn canal boats had to be raised a total of 233 feet. This was accomplished with twenty-nine lift locks. With the canal boat moving about three miles per hour and encountering a lock about every mile and a half, the trip took a couple of days.

Admission
No entry fee. Open Sundays, 1 P.M.–5 P.M., April–October.

NORTH EAST
Upper Bay Museum

Upper Bay Museum
Walnut Street
North East, MD 21901
(301) 287-5718

Location
Take the SR-272 exit off I-95, heading south one mile to North East.

Highlights
Sculling oar collection
History of water-related industry
History of local area hunting

General Information
The upper Chesapeake Bay enjoys a rich history of maritime activity. Water-related industry and commerce have long been important to local economic vitality, and for over 100 years watermen have earned their livelihood from the bounty of the Bay.

Today, the heritage and progress of Bay boating and fishing are exhibited in the Upper Bay Museum's collection of antique marine engines, among the best in the country. Also displayed are mahogany miniatures that depict the vessels that have long plied these waters.

The museum also houses an extensive collection of hunting, fishing, and boating artifacts from the upper Bay region, including an important sculling oar collection. Some fifty oars are on display—the type used principally on bushwack rigs—which ensured that duck hunters would leave the waters undisturbed and glide along almost soundlessly.

Activities
Artists' demonstrations, competitions, displays, and auctions

Admission
No entry fee, but donations accepted. Open Sundays only, 9 A.M.–4 P.M., Memorial Day–Labor Day. Other times by appointment.

OXFORD
Oxford Museum

Oxford Museum, Inc.
Morris and Market Streets
Oxford, MD 21654
(301) 226-5331

Location
Take the SR-333 exit off Rte. 50 on Maryland's Eastern Shore. Bear west five miles into Oxford. The museum is at the corner of Morris and Market Streets.

Highlights
Home of Robert Morris
Port of Entry (publication)

General Information
The Oxford Museum, founded in 1964, is a personal marine museum with mementos dating from the time when Robert Morris, the financier of the American Revolution, lived in the house that the museum now occupies. Many items displayed in the museum pertain to the fact that Oxford was the first port of entry in Maryland.

Admission
No entry fee. Open Friday–Sunday, 2 P.M.–5 P.M., April–October.

PINEY POINT

Harry Lundberg School of Seamanship

Harry Lundberg School of Seamanship
Piney Point, MD 20674
(301) 994-0010

Location
Follow Rte. 301 south from Washington, D.C., forty miles to the junction of SR-234. Head east twenty-two miles to the junction of SR-249. Head south to Piney Point on the Potomac River, fifteen miles upstream from the Chesapeake Bay.

Highlights
The *Manitou* (yacht)

General Information
Harry Lundberg School of Seamanship is a merchant marine training school. Several vessels including the *Manitou,* sailed by the late President John F. Kennedy, are on exhibit.

Admission
No entry fee. Open the first Sunday of every month, 9 A.M.–5 P.M.

POTOMAC
Chesapeake and Ohio Canal Tavern Museum

C and O Canal Foundry Mall
30th and M Streets, N.W.
Washington, DC
(202) 472-4376

Chesapeake and Ohio Canal Tavern Museum
11710 MacArthur Boulevard
Potomac, MD 20854
(301) 299-3613

C and O National Historical Park
P.O. Box 4
Sharpsburg, MD 21782
(301) 739-4206

Location
Travel eleven miles northwest of Washington, D.C., on Rte. 190 to Potomac.

Highlights
Seneca lockhouse and aqueducts
Canal barge trips
Paw Paw Tunnel tour

General Information
The Chesapeake and Ohio Canal Tavern Museum was founded in 1954 as a canal history museum housed in the 1830 Crommelin House, originally a hotel owned by the Chesapeake and Ohio

Canal Company. Collections include historical photographs and artifacts pertaining to the working canal and its families. Exhibits are also contained in lockhouse 49, the 1830 Great Falls Tavern Museum, and Abner Cloud house.

Additionally, the Chesapeake and Ohio Canal National Historic Park, founded in 1971, stretches for 184.5 miles from Georgetown (Washington, D.C.) to Cumberland, Md. The canal parallels the Potomac River, offering countless sites of incredible beauty and a wealth of historical data. Locks and lockhouses, dams, aqueducts, mule barns, and remnants of once-thriving communities remind us of the almost 100 years (1828–1924) of active canal traffic.

Seventy-four lift locks were built, each one 100 feet long, 15 feet wide, and 16 feet deep and capable of lifting or lowering boats 8 feet. A set of wooden lock gates, weighing over two tons, were at each end of the lock. Originally, numbers identified the locks, but numbers gave way to names like Swains Lock and Pennyfield Lock. Eleven aqueducts built between Georgetown and Cumberland allowed numerous tributaries to flow into the Potomac River, some even flowing under the canal.

To avoid a six-mile bend in the Potomac, canal builders bored through a knobby spur in a mountain and created the Paw Paw Tunnel. It is 3,118 feet long and took fourteen years to build (1836–50). It is situated ten miles east of Oldtown, Md., on SR-51.

Activities

Films, educational walks and talks, and living history demonstrations at Seneca lockhouse. The National Park Service sponsors one-and-a-half-hour trips aboard a replica barge on the historic canal from Georgetown and Great Falls, Md. Along the way, men and women in period costumes relate the history of the canal, lead group singing, and tell anecdotes. (For information on these boat trips, phone 301-299-9006.)

Admission

No entry fee for the museum. Open daily, 9 A.M.–5 P.M., year-round. Closed Christmas. Please check at the Foundry Mall in Georgetown (Washington, D.C.) and the park in Sharpsburg, Md., for their opening hours.

ST. MICHAELS
Chesapeake Bay Maritime Museum

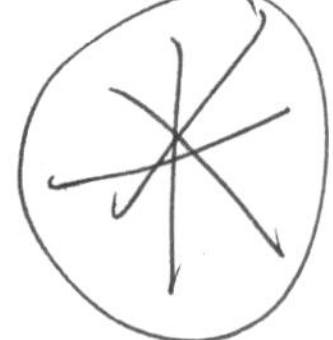

Chesapeake Bay Maritime Museum
P.O. Box 636
St. Michaels, MD 21663
(301) 745-2916

Location
This museum complex is located on a peninsula in the harbor of historic and picturesque St. Michaels on the Eastern Shore. From the Bay Bridge follow Rte. 50 east to the Easton bypass (SR-322 south). Bear west on SR-33 into St. Michaels, turning right onto Mill Street.

Highlights
Hooper Strait Lighthouse
Aquarium
Wooden boatbuilding
Weather Gauge (semi-annual publication)
On the Beam (newsletter)
Library (2,500 volumes)
Museum store

General Information
The Chesapeake Bay Maritime Museum is dedicated to preserving the history of the Chesapeake Bay region. The museum has grown from a single house in 1965, when it was established, to a sixteen-acre complex of restored buildings and new structures erected to exhibit a comprehensive collection of Bay artifacts and to preserve the lore of the area.

Exhibits include: a floating collection of historic Chesapeake Bay craft; an aquarium of Bay life; the Hooper Strait Lighthouse; a working boat shop; and a working decoy and mounted waterfowl exhibit, along with other Bay memorabilia.

Displays at the museum trace the history of the Bay and its traditions in boatbuilding, commercial fishing, yachting, waterfowling, and navigation. Major features include a 100-year-old "screwpile" lighthouse, a restored log-bottom bugeye, a skipjack, a racing canoe, an important collection of Bay small craft, and a comprehensive decoy and waterfowling presentation.

Activities
Research projects, education classes (including wooden boat-building), seminars, and maritime history

Admission
Entry fee. Memberships (one with special docking privileges) are available. Open daily, 10 A.M.–5 P.M. in the summer; 10 A.M.–4 P.M. in the winter. Open Saturdays and Sundays only, January, February, and early March.

SOLOMONS
Calvert Marine Museum

Calvert Marine Museum
Route 2
P.O. Box 97
Solomons, MD 20688
(301) 326-2042

Location
Solomons is at the mouth of the Patuxent River (the first river north of the Potomac River) on the Chesapeake Bay. Take SR-4 south off of Rte. 301 (east of Washington, D.C.).

Highlights
Drum Point Lighthouse
The *Wm. B. Tennison* (historic bugeye)
Small-craft collection
Art collection
J. C. Lore Oyster Processing Plant
Bugeye Times (newsletter)
Library (1,600 volumes on maritime history)

General Information
The Calvert Marine Museum was founded in 1969. It is ideally situated for interpreting the natural history of this tidewater region as it has evolved from prehistory through human utilization. The museum relates its three areas of interest—paleontology, estuarine biology, and marine history—to the public in an educational

manner, maintaining a repository of specimens and artifacts pertinent to these themes and stimulating research in these areas for better understanding and more accurate documentation of the estuarine and cultural history of the region.

Drum Point Lighthouse dominates the museum's waterfront. Constructed in 1883 at Drum Point to mark the entrance to the Patuxent River, this screwpile cottage-type light is one of only three that remain of the forty-five that once served the Chesapeake Bay at the turn of the century. Decommissioned in 1962, the lighthouse fell victim to vandals until it was moved in 1975 to its present site. Authentically restored, it has become the museum's main attraction.

The marine museum is housed in a new 30,000-square-foot exhibition building on the waterfront. Exhibits include: vessels constructed by an important local commercial boatbuilding enterprise; a fine art collection; a historic 1899 log oyster boat; and a 1,600-volume library on maritime history. Also exhibited are artifacts excavated from a vessel of the Chesapeake Flotilla, which defended the Chesapeake during the War of 1812.

The J. C. Lore Oyster Processing Plant, a half mile south, provides a look at commercial fishing in the region from the perspective of people engaged in the industry.

Activities

Guided tours, lectures, craft demonstrations, slide and film programs, field trips, educational programs, boat rides, and a special hands-on discovery room for young visitors.

Admission

No entry fee. Memberships are available. Open Monday–Saturday, 10 A.M.–5 P.M., Sunday, noon–5 P.M., May–September; Monday–Friday, 10 A.M.–4:30 P.M., Saturdays–Sundays, noon–4:30 P.M. the rest of the year. Closed Thanksgiving, Christmas, and New Year's Day. (Discovery Room hours vary.)

An entry fee is charged at Drum Point Lighthouse. It is open Monday–Saturday, 10 A.M.–5 P.M., Sunday, noon–5 P.M., May–September. (Winter hours are different). The J. C. Lore Oyster House also charges an entry fee, and its hours are the same as at the lighthouse.

VIRGINIA

ALEXANDRIA
Alexandria Seaport Foundation

Alexandria Seaport Foundation
1000 South Lee Street
Alexandria, VA 22314
(703) 549-7080

Location
Alexandria is just south of Washington, D.C., off I-495. The foundation is on Alexandria's waterfront at the foot of Prince Street near the downtown area.

The second *New Jersey* (BB-62) was launched 7 December 1942 in Philadelphia. She first saw action in January 1944 in the South Pacific. Mothballed after World War II, she was recommissioned in November 1950 and remains an active part of the U.S. Fleet. (Photo: Jerry MacMullen Library, Maritime Museum of San Diego.)

Highlights
The *Alexandria* (schooner)
Wooden boatbuilding

General Information
Our country has been built upon a proud maritime tradition, and decades ago, the city of Alexandria was one of America's largest seaports. The Alexandria Seaport Foundation, through its Compass Rose Program, was founded to preserve this proud heritage. The schooner *Alexandria* was acquired in 1983 to help fulfill this mandate. Formerly the *Lindo*, she is a classic Scandinavian cargo vessel built in Sweden in 1929, then remodeled for passengers in the early 1970s.

Admission
Entry fee. *Alexandria* is open to the public Saturdays and Sundays, 1 P.M.–5 P.M., when in port. Call or write the foundation for more information.

Alexandria Waterfront Museum

Alexandria Waterfront Museum
Office of Historic Alexandria
P.O. Box 178, City Hall
Alexandria, VA 22313
(703) 838-4288/4554

Location
The museum is located on Montgomery Street, east off of North Fairfax Street in Alexandria. It adjoins the TransPotomac Canal Center in historic Old Town.

Highlights
Canal history
Canal
Library

General Information
The Alexandria Waterfront Museum, founded in 1988, interprets the development of the city's waterfront and the maritime activi-

ties from its founding in 1749 to the present. It is located along the route of the Alexandria Canal, which operated from 1843 until 1886.

In addition to the seven-mile canal, the museum's first major exhibit, entitled "Trade and Prosperity: The Alexandria Canal," includes model canal boats, drawings, paintings, historical documents, and educational materials that pertain to the canal.

Activities
A video presentation of the archaeological excavation of Lift Lock 1 before restoration

Admission
No entry fee. Open Tuesday–Friday, 11 A.M.–4 P.M., Saturdays and Sundays, 1 P.M.–4 P.M., year-round.

Torpedo Factory Art Center

Torpedo Factory Art Center
105 North Union Street
Alexandria, VA 22314
(703) 838-4565

Location
From Washington, D.C., take SR-400 south past National Airport to King Street. Head east toward the intersection with North Union Street. The museum is on the Potomac River in historic Old Town Alexandria.

Highlights
Torpedo Factory history
Art Center

General Information
The Torpedo Factory Art Center, founded in 1974, is an art museum housed in a world wars I and II torpedo factory. It consists of eighty-four artist's studios, four cooperative galleries, an Art League School, and the Alexandria Archaeology Center. Collections and displays emphasize the history of the factory and include torpedoes and related objects.

Activities
Guided tours, lectures, films, and concerts.

Admission
No entry fee. Open daily, 10 A.M.–5 P.M., year-round. Closed Thanksgiving, Christmas, and New Year's Day.

CHINCOTEAGUE
The Oyster Museum

Oyster Museum
P.O. Box 4
Chincoteague, VA 23336
(804) 336-6117

Location
Chincoteague sits across from the southern tip of Assateague Island. Take Rte. 13 north/south to the Delmarva Peninsula, just south of the Maryland state line on the Atlantic coast. The museum is on Maddox Boulevard in the town center.

Highlights
Shellfish farming and seafood industry

General Information
The Oyster Museum exhibits (including a narrated diaorama) depict the history of oystering from the 1600s to the present. There are shell collections, displays on predators of the oyster, and the tools used by oystermen. Of special note is the history of Chincoteague Island.

Admission
Entry fee. Open daily, 10 A.M.–4:45 P.M., Memorial Day–Labor Day; Saturdays and Sundays, 11 A.M.–4:45 P.M., 1 April–Memorial Day and after Labor Day–30 September.

GREAT FALLS
The Patowmack Canal

The Patowmack Canal
National Park Service
Great Falls, VA 22066
(703) 759-2915

Location
The Patowmack Canal is located at Great Falls Park, Virginia, which is fifteen miles northwest of Washington, D.C., at the end of Old Dominion Drive, and four miles west of I-495 on Rte. 193.

Highlights
Interpretive center

General Information
An entire town grew up around the canal construction site at Great Falls to serve as headquarters for the Patowmack Company and home for the workers. Founded by the Revolutionary War hero "Light Horse" Harry Lee and named for his first wife, Matildaville boasted at its height the company superintendent's house, a market, gristmill, sawmill, foundry, inn, icehouse, workers' barracks, boarding houses, and a sprinkling of small homes. Although the Patowmack Company was a financial failure, the canal builders pioneered lock engineering and stimulated a wave of canal construction important to the country's development.

Things to see include a wing dam, upper guard gate, dry-laid walls, gristmill, iron forge, locks 1, 2, 3, 4, and 5, and Mather Gorge.

Admission
No entry fee. Open for guided tours Saturdays, 11 A.M., year-round.

NEWPORT NEWS
The Mariners Museum

The Mariners Museum
100 Museum Drive
Newport News, VA 23606
(804) 595-0368

Location
Newport News lies at the southern end of the Chesapeake Bay, just twenty minutes southeast of Williamsburg. Take exit 62A off I-64 onto Rte. 17 and follow the signs to the museum's entrance.

Highlights
Japanese submarine
Small craft collection
Ship models
Restored engine room from an 1895 steam tug
Figureheads
Paintings
Hands-on exhibits
Library (67,000 volumes, 350,000 photographs)

General Information
The Mariners Museum, founded in 1930, preserves and interprets the story of mankind's relationship with the sea through its international collection of figureheads, ship models, small craft, paintings, scrimshaw, and other maritime artifacts. The scope and depth of the museum's collections has made it one of the best maritime museums in the world.

Ten galleries at the museum interpret more than three thousand years of nautical experience on streams, bays, and oceans. The Great Hall of Steam showcases the museum's extensive model ship collection. The many uses of such models are examined in a separate gallery. Of special significance is the August F. Crabtree Collection of Miniature Ships. Sixteen models illustrate the evolution of vessel design. Other exhibits include the role of marine artists and the story of Western seapower in the "Battle of the Ironclads," some of which are located in the recently opened Chesapeake Bay Gallery in a new exhibition wing at the museum.

Complementing the museum is an exceptional library and research facility that houses one of the most complete collections of maritime-related materials in the country.

Activities
Guided tours of the ten galleries, lectures, and slide/film shows

Admission
Entry fee. Open Monday–Saturday, 9 A.M.–5 P.M., Sundays, noon–5 P.M., year-round. Closed Christmas.

NORFOLK
Hampton Roads Naval Museum

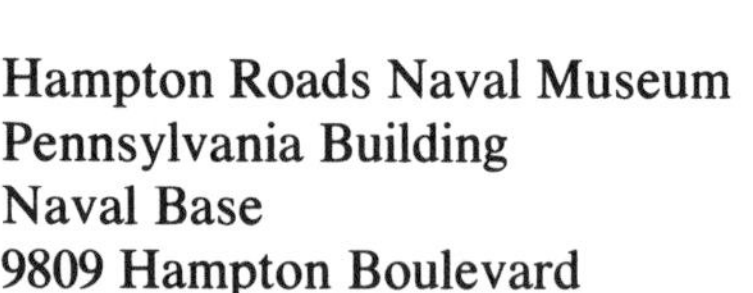

Hampton Roads Naval Museum
Pennsylvania Building
Naval Base
9809 Hampton Boulevard
Norfolk, VA 23511-6002
(804) 444-3827

Location
The naval museum is located on the grounds of the Norfolk Naval Base, which can be reached by taking I-64 north/south to I-564 north into Norfolk.

Highlights
Archaeological artifacts
Ship and aircraft models
Period photographs
Gift shop

General Information
Hampton Roads Naval Museum, founded in 1979, is housed in the historic Pennsylvania Building, a two-thirds replica of Independence Hall built for the Jamestown Tercentennial Exposition of 1907. Its collections include naval artifacts and artworks, ship and aircraft models built to scale, electric maps, a film, and a NATO exhibit.

The *United States,* the fastest commercial ship ever built. She sailed her maiden voyage from New York to South Hampton 3 July 1952 at over 35 knots, breaking all North Atlantic speed records. In 1973 the U.S. Maritime Administration purchased the *United States,* and she has laid up at Norfolk, Virginia, ever since. (Photo: Jerry MacMullen Library, Maritime Museum of San Diego.)

Activities
Allow thirty minutes for a self-guided tour; lectures, and slide presentations. Buses may load and unload in front of the museum. Passes may be picked up at the tour office.

Admission
No entry fee. Open daily, 9 A.M.–4 P.M., year-round. Closed Thanksgiving, Christmas, and New Year's Day.

ONANCOCK
Hopkins and Bros. Store

Hopkins and Bros. Store
2 Market Street
Onancock, VA 23417
(804) 787-8220

Location
Onancock lies sixty-four miles northeast of Norfolk (across the Chesapeake Bay Bridge-Tunnel) on the Delmarva (DELaware, MARyland, VirginiA) Peninsula. Follow Rte. 13 out of Norfolk.

Highlights
Early marine general store
Restaurant

General Information
Hopkins and Bros. Store, founded in 1838, is an architectural museum with original furnishings. As a marine general store it dates back to 1842, when Captain Stephen Hopkins built it, thus beginning a family business which spanned four generations and 125 years. As one of the oldest general stores on the East Coast, it is both a Virginian and an American historic landmark.

Activities
Cruise trips to Tangier Island

Admission
No entry fee. Open 8:30 A.M.–9 P.M., 1 June–Labor Day; 8:30 A.M.–4:30 P.M., the day after Labor Day–31 May.

PORTSMOUTH

Portsmouth Lightship Museum

(*See also:* Portsmouth Naval Shipyard Museum)

Portsmouth Lightship Museum
London Slip at Water Street
P.O. Box 248
Portsmouth, VA 23705
(804) 393-8741/8591

Location
Portsmouth lies immediately to the west of Norfolk on the Elizabeth River. The museum is on Water Street at the foot of Lundow Boulevard (one block from the Portsmouth Naval Shipyard Museum), just off I-264.

Highlights
The *Portsmouth* (lightship)

General Information
The *Portsmouth* Lightship Museum, formerly in the U.S. Lightship Service and later the U.S. Coast Guard, exhibits the important functions of lightships in maritime history. Visitors will experience the history of the heralded Lightship Service that began off Portsmouth's Craney Island in 1820. The lightship has been painstakingly restored to its original condition and was designated a national historic landmark in 1989.

Visitors will likewise see how lightship crew members lived and worked, where they dined, and the quarters where they slept. The galley is fully stocked and ready for sea duty. A large windlass room adjoins the crew members' spartan living quarters. Magnificent lenses, some nearly a century old, designed to warn ships miles away of dangerous sea conditions are also on display.

The *Portsmouth* lightship, measuring 101 feet, 10 inches in length and 25 feet, 8 inches across, with a 360-ton water displacement, originally served off Cape Charles after she was commissioned in 1915.

Admission
No entry fee. Open Tuesday–Saturday, 10 A.M.–5 P.M., Sunday, 1 P.M.–5 P.M., year-round. Closed Thanksgiving, Christmas, and New Year's Day.

Portsmouth Naval Shipyard Museum

(*See also: Portsmouth* Lightship Museum)

Portsmouth Naval Shipyard Museum
2 High Street
P.O. Box 248
Portsmouth, VA 23705
(804) 393-8591

Location
Portsmouth is immediately west of Norfolk on the Elizabeth River. Its naval shipyard lies at the foot of High Street off I-264.

Highlights
The CSS *Virginia* model (formerly the *Merrimac*)
The US *Delaware*
Ship models
Library (6,000 volumes)
Gift shop

General Information
The Portsmouth Naval Shipyard Museum, founded in 1949, is on the Elizabeth River waterfront. Paintings, models, and exhibits trace the history of the U.S. Navy, with an emphasis on local history and armed forces in the area. Particularly noteworthy are the models of the CSS *Virginia,* the U.S. ship of the line *Delaware,* and the model of Portsmouth as it appeared in 1776.

Collections include: history of the naval shipyard and the armed forces of the locality; the CSS *Virginia,* also known as the *Merrimac;* ship models, uniforms, flags, and arms of all types; and early regional maps, prints, memorabilia, and model planes.

A library of general reference books is available for research by appointment.

Activities
Guided tours

Admission
No entry fee. Open Tuesday–Saturday, 10 A.M.–5 P.M., Sunday, 1 P.M.–5 P.M., year-round. Closed Thanksgiving, Christmas, and New Year's Day.

VIRGINIA BEACH
Cape Henry Lighthouse

Cape Henry Lighthouse
P.O. Box 5064
Virginia Beach, VA 23455
(804) 460-1688

Location
In Virginia Beach, the lighthouse is six miles north on Rte. 60 (or seven miles east of the junction of Rtes. 60 and 13).

Highlights
Cape Henry Lighthouse

General Information
The Cape Henry Lighthouse, founded in 1791, is the first commissioned public works building in the United States, built near the monument that marks the first landing of the Jamestown colonists. The facilities include the lighthouse and the Lynnhaven House.

Admission
Entry fee. Combination tickets for the lighthouse and the Lynnhaven House. Open daily, 10 A.M.–dusk, Memorial Day–Labor Day.

Maritime Historical Museum

Maritime Historical Museum
Attn: Officer in Charge
25th Street and Atlantic Avenue
Virginia Beach, VA 23451
(804) 491-8608

Location
The museum is just twelve miles east of Norfolk via Rte. 58 or SR-44 (tollway).

Highlights
Maritime history
Scrimshaw

General Information
Housed in the Old Seatack Coast Guard Station, the Maritime Historical Museum was built in 1903 and is now a historic landmark. The station exhibits nautical artifacts, scrimshaw, photographs, and a *Norwegian Lady* display.

Admission
Call or write the museum for information about their opening hours.

Old and New Lighthouses

Old and New Lighthouses
Fort Story
Virginia Beach, VA 23459
(804) 422-7305

Location
From Norfolk, take Rte. 60 east the eighteen miles to Fort Story.

Highlights
Lighthouses

General Information
Old Lighthouse is within the Fort Story army post adjacent to the Cape Henry Memorial. Built in 1791–92, the lighthouse was the first one erected by the United States.

New Lighthouse, erected in 1881, has one of the most powerful lights in the world. It sits 157 feet above sea level and is visible for twenty miles.

Admission
Visitors' passes to Fort Story are issued at the East Gate (at the north end of Atlantic Avenue) or at the West Gate (on Rte. 60).

Life-Saving Museum of Virginia

Life-Saving Museum of Virginia
24th Street and Oceanfront
P.O. Box 24
Virginia Beach, VA 23451
(804) 422-1587

Location
The museum is located at 24th Street and Oceanfront in Virginia Beach, twelve miles east of Norfolk.

Highlights
Ship models
Shipwreck exhibit
"War Years" (World War II exhibit)

Scrimshaw
The Keeper (newsletter)

General Information
The Life-Saving Museum of Virginia, founded in 1980, is housed in a restored former U.S. Lifesaving Service and Coast Guard Station (c. 1903). It is the only existing station in Virginia—among a mere handful on the entire Atlantic coast—now open to the public, preserving the history of these lifesaving services. Visitors to the museum's galleries are given a rare insight into the early days of shipwrecks and lifesaving efforts. Visual exhibits of many of these wrecks along the city's shoreline tell tales of bravery and sometimes disaster.

An extensive collection of maritime memorabilia and scrimshaw are featured, as are changing displays. Collections include ship models, photographs, maritime artifacts, maritime art, audio-visual programs, and uniforms. The upper gallery (added in 1989) contains an exhibit on America's involvement in World War II.

Activities
Guided tours, lectures, films, concerts, and workshops

Admission
Entry fee. Memberships are available. Open Monday–Saturday, 10 A.M.–9 P.M., Sunday, noon–5 P.M., Memorial Day–Labor Day; Tuesday–Saturday, 10 A.M.–5 P.M., Sunday, noon–5 P.M., October–Memorial Day. Closed Thanksgiving, Christmas, New Year's Eve, and New Year's Day.

WILLIAMSBURG
Jamestown Settlement

Jamestown Settlement
Post Office Drawer JF
Williamsburg, VA 23187
(804) 229-1607

Location
The settlement is six miles from historic Williamsburg, just off SR-31.

Highlights
The *Godspeed, Susan Constant,* and *Discovery* (replica ships)

General Information
The dramatic story of the founding of America's first permanent English settlement and its impact on native American culture is told at Jamestown Settlement, a living history museum on the banks of the James River in Tidewater Virginia. The Jamestown Settlement is located about a mile from the original site of Jamestown, established thirteen years before the Pilgrims landed at Plymouth in 1620.

A pathway leads from the fort to a pier where full-scale reproductions of the three square-rigged sailing ships that transported 104 colonists—all men and boys—to Virginia in 1607 are docked. Visitors can board and explore the largest, the 110-foot *Susan Constant,* and listen to a costumed guide talk about the four-and-a-half-month voyage from England and navigational techniques used by seventeenth-century mariners to sail across the ocean.

Alongside the *Susan Constant* are the smaller *Godspeed* and the tiny *Discovery.* In 1985 the Jamestown-Yorktown Foundation sponsored a reenactment of the *Godspeed*'s voyage.

Admission
Entry fee. Open daily, 9 A.M.–5 P.M., year-round. Closed Christmas and New Year's Day.

WASHINGTON, D.C.

The Navy Museum

The Navy Museum
Building No. 76
Washington Navy Yard
9th and M Streets, S.E.
Washington, DC 20374-0571
(202) 433-3017

Location
The museum is on the grounds of the Washington Navy Yard, south of the downtown area on 9th and M Streets, Southeast.

Highlights
The USS *Barry* (DD 933) (destroyer)
F4U Corsair
Submarine periscopes
World War II gun mounts
Naval Historical Center (research library and archives)

General Information
The Navy Museum, founded in 1961 and previously known as the Navy Memorial Museum, was opened to collect, preserve, and display naval artifacts, models, documents, and fine art. Through its exhibits the museum chronicles the history of the U.S. Navy from the American Revolution to the present. The exhibits commemorate the navy's wartime heroes and battles as well as its peacetime contributions in such fields as exploration, diplomacy, space flight, navigation, and humanitarian service. Tools, equipment, and personal artifacts offer the visitor a unique opportunity to gain an understanding of naval customs, ways of life, and contributions to society.

Located in the historic Washington Navy Yard, the Navy Museum is housed in the former Breech Mechanism Shop of the old gun factory. Built between 1887 and 1899, the 600-foot-long building was one of several shops in the yard that produced ordnance, missile components, and electronic equipment until 1962.

Recently, all of the exhibits and archives of the Truxtun-Decatur Naval Museum were moved to the Navy Museum. Included were prints, photographs, ship models, and uniforms. The museum is part of the Naval Historical Center, which includes a library, archives, and other research facilities.

Activities
Self-guided and guided tours, and a seafaring celebration each fall

Admission
No entry fee. Open Monday–Friday, 9 A.M.–5 P.M., Memorial Day–Labor Day); 9 A.M.–4 P.M., the rest of the year; Saturdays, Sundays, and holidays year-round, 10 A.M.–5 P.M.

Smithsonian Institution

Curator of Maritime History
Division of Transportation
National Museum of American History
Washington, DC 20560
(202) 357-2025

Location
The Smithsonian's museums line the Mall in Washington, D.C., between the George Washington Monument and the Capitol.

Highlights
Hall of American Maritime Enterprise
Hall of Armed Forces History

General Information
The Smithsonian Institution houses its maritime exhibits in the Hall of American Maritime Enterprise and the Hall of Armed Forces History. Models and graphics show the development of water commerce, inland waterways, the development of steam and sail, and various other exhibits relating to American maritime service.

Research facilities include drawings by Howard I. Chapelle, the Historic American Merchant Marine Survey, the Cropley Collection (maritime clipping file), and photo files.

Note: The Division of Transportation also offers a catalog of ship plans from which watercraft designs can be ordered at nominal fees. Write for information.

Activities
Research facilities (admission by appointment only, weekdays between 10 A.M.–4:30 P.M.)

Admission
No entry fee. Open daily, 10 A.M.–5:30 P.M., year-round. Closed Christmas.

THREE

SOUTHEAST

NORTH CAROLINA

BEAUFORT
North Carolina Maritime Museum

North Carolina Maritime Museum
315 Front Street
Beaufort, NC 26156
(919) 728-7317

Location
From Raleigh take Rte. 70 southeast approximately 140 miles to Beaufort, passing through Goldsboro, Kinston, and New Bern. The museum is on the inland waterway just east of Morehead City.

Highlights
Historic Beaufort (1709), a restored North Carolinian seaport
Ship models
Wooden boatbuilding
The Waterline (newsletter)
Library
Gift shop, bookstore, NOAA chart shop

General Information
The North Carolina Maritime Museum, founded in 1975 but first established in 1951 as the Hampton Marine Museum, contains mounted marine specimens, seashells, aquaria, ship models, marine artifacts, and a small-craft collection.

The museum's varied programming, which reflects the museum's joint themes of maritime and coastal natural history, has achieved a level of excellence in both education and entertainment that is recognized nationwide. The "Traditional Wooden Boat Show" and the "Strange Seafood Exhibition" are annual museum programs. "Summer Science School for Children," coastal habitat field trips, and special programs are but a few examples of the unique activities provided by the museum. In addition, there are a boatshop and a substantial ship's library of plans, charts, and volumes on traditional boatbuilding.

Activities
Lectures, year-round field trips, and special programs

Admission
No entry fee. Memberships are available. Open Monday–Friday, 9 A.M.–5 P.M., Saturday, 10 A.M.–5 P.M., Sunday 2 P.M.–5 P.M., year-round. Closed Christmas and New Year's Day.

CAPE HATTERAS NATIONAL SEASHORE

Museum of the Sea and Hatteras Island Visitor's Center

Museum of the Sea and Hatteras Island Visitor's Center
Buxton, NC 27920
(919) 995-4474

Location
Cape Hatteras National Seashore is approachable by land and water. Coming from the south, entry is via a Cedar Island ferry or the Swan Quarter toll ferry; from the north, via Rtes. 158 and 12 south; from the west, via Rtes. 64 and 12 south. A free ferry travels between Ocracoke Island and Hatteras. The visitor's center is in Buxton, on the southern tip of the island.

Highlights
History of life on Hatteras Island
Cape Hatteras Lighthouse

General Information
The Museum of the Sea, founded in 1953, exhibits history, natural history, historic houses circa 1870, Cape Hatteras Lighthouse (1870), and the lighthouse keeper's dwellings. Collections include maps, charts, and maritime artifacts. The Visitor's Center is the restored keeper's quarters.

The thin strand of Cape Hatteras National Seashore, seventy miles long, winds between the windy, pounding Atlantic and the shallow Pamlico Sound.

Activities
Guided tours and lectures

Admission
No entry fee. Open daily, 9 A.M.–5 P.M., year-round.

KINSTON
Caswell-Neuse State Historic Site

Caswell-Neuse State Historic Site
P.O. Box 3043
Kinston, NC 28501
(919) 522-2091

Location
Southeast of Raleigh approximately eighty miles, Kinston is equidistant between Virginia and South Carolina.

Highlights
The CSS *Neuse* (ironclad hull)
Nautical blacksmithing

General Information
Caswell-Neuse State Historic Site, founded in 1965, includes: a museum; a memorial to Richard Caswell, the first Governor of North Carolina; and the sunken ram CSS *Neuse,* one of two remaining Confederate naval vessels.

Union forces had already taken several small forts and port towns in North Carolina when the Confederate States Navy commissioned the construction of the gunboat *Neuse* (c. 1862–65). She was one of twenty-two Confederate ironclad ramming vessels built. The existing hull measures 136 feet long and 37 feet wide.

The museum presents exhibits and a slide show that unfold the story of the Neuse. Nautical blacksmithing and nineteenth-century ropemaking are also demonstrated.

Activities
Guided tours, lectures, audiovisual programs, and a sound-and-light show depicting the governor's life and times.

Admission
No entry fee. Open Monday–Saturday, 9 A.M.–5 P.M., Sunday, 1 P.M.–5 P.M., year-round. Closed Thanksgiving, Christmas Eve, and Christmas.

MANTEO
Elizabeth II State Historic Site

Elizabeth II State Historic Site
P.O. Box 155
Manteo, NC 27954
(919) 473-1144

Location
From Rocky Mount take Rte. 64 east approximately 154 miles to Manteo, on Roanoke Island across from the Manteo waterfront on Rte. 400.

Highlights
The *Elizabeth II*
Volunteer crew training program
Visitor's Center and giftshop

General Information
The *Elizabeth II* State Historic Site is a museum about life in the sixteenth century. Exhibits both inside and outside the Visitor's Center, together with a twenty-minute multimedia program, orient visitors to the Roanoke voyages and life aboard a sixteenth-century ship. Professionally trained guides assist visitors and prepare them, in the summer season, to meet men who portray—in dress, speech, manner, and attitudes—mariners and colonists from Raleigh's voyages.

Between 1584 and 1587 Sir Walter Raleigh sponsored three voyages to the New World. The first was to explore the area; the second was to establish a military colony; and the objective of the third voyage was to found a settlement. The *Elizabeth II* is named for one of the seven vessels that sailed in the second expedition in 1585.

Activities
Ship's tour

Admission
Entry fee. Open Tuesday–Sunday, 10 A.M.–4 P.M., November–April; 10 A.M.–6 P.M., May–October.

WILMINGTON
New Hanover County Museum of Lower Cape Fear

New Hanover County Museum
814 Market Street
Wilmington, NC 28401
(919) 763-0852

Location
Take Rte. 74/76 to Wilmington, in southeastern North Carolina. The museum is eight blocks east of the Cape Fear River on Market Street.

Highlights
Ship models
Newsletter
Gift shop

General Information
Founded in 1898, the New Hanover County Museum contains a collection of Civil War artifacts and nineteenth- and twentieth-century photographs, books, textiles, and toys. Since its modest beginning, it has evolved into a museum with a collection of over 13,000 artifacts, including ship models, small arms, paintings, ship guns, and relics salvaged from sunken vessels. "The Wilmington Waterfront," a diorama of the Wilmington riverfront in 1863, shows blockade runners, shipyards, sail lofts, and warehouses. Relating to this central model are separate exhibits examining imported goods, naval stores, and cotton industries.

Activities
Sunday programs and special classes are frequently offered

Admission
No entry fee. Open Tuesday–Saturday, 9 A.M.–5 P.M., Sunday, 2 P.M.–5 P.M., year-round. Closed national holidays.

USS *North Carolina* Battleship Memorial

USS *North Carolina* Battleship Memorial
P.O. Box 417
Wilmington, NC 28402
(919) 762-1829

Location
Take Rte. 74/76 to Wilmington, in southeastern North Carolina. The battleship is moored at Eagle Island on the Cape Fear River, just three miles from downtown Wilmington.

Highlights
The USS *North Carolina* (battleship)
Kingfisher floatplane
Paintings and photographs
Summertime evening sound-and-light show
Souvenir shop

General Information
The USS *North Carolina* Battleship Memorial was founded in 1961 and is dedicated to all the men and women who have served in the U.S. military, particularly those North Carolinians who died in World War II. At the time of her commissioning on 9 April 1941, the USS *North Carolina* was considered the most powerful sea weapon in the world.

Visitors may view the gun turrets, galley, engine room, wheelhouse, machine shop, pilothouse, crew's quarters, mess hall, sick bay, and a restored Vought Kingfisher floatplane. The museum displays photographs and artifacts of the ship's participation in every major naval offensive in the Pacific during World War II and includes the Roll of Honor of 10,000 North Carolinians who lost their lives in that war.

Activities
Self-guided tours, orientation film, summer drama

Admission
Entry fee. Open daily, 8 A.M.–8 P.M. in summer; 8 A.M.–sunset in winter. Sound-and-light show nightly, 9 P.M., June–Labor Day.

TENNESSEE

MEMPHIS
Mississippi River Museum at Mud Island

Mississippi River Museum at Mud Island
125 North Front Street
Memphis, TN 38103
(901) 576-7230

Location
The museum is adjacent to downtown Memphis, just north of I-40 across the Wolf River.

Highlights
Civil War gunboat and riverboat
Scale model of the river

General Information
The Mississippi River Museum at Mud Island, founded in 1978, exhibits reconstructions of a riverboat and Civil War gunboat with period furnishings; artifacts and archives relating to prehistoric and historic Indians, settlement, and boat development; Civil War music; boat models and engines; river engineering; natural

history and sciences; a related art collection; an outdoor exhibition; a five-block-long scale model of the river, focusing on the cultural and natural history of the lower Mississippi River.

Activities
Guided tours, lectures, films, gallery talks, and concerts

Admission
Entry fee. Call or write the museum for information about their opening hours.

SOUTH CAROLINA

CHARLESTON
Charles Towne Landing

Charles Towne Landing
1500 Old Town Road
Charleston, SC 29407-6099
(803) 556-4450

Location
Charles Towne Landing is located six miles northwest of Charleston on SR-171, about a fifteen-minute drive from the city's center.

Highlights
The *Adventure* (trading ketch)
The *Carolina* (sailing ship model)
Newsletter

General Information
Charles Towne Landing was founded in 1970 along the historic Ashley River where much of Charleston's wealth originated and its plantation system flourished. Here, over 300 years ago, the first permanent English settlement in South Carolina was established.

The museum displays collections of pre-1775 historic artifacts, the trading ketch *Adventure* (1670), and a collection of dugouts, nine canoes (from the most primitive to a large shad-fishing size), each one carved from a cypress log.

Nearby, Drayton Hall, a stately plantation house begun in 1738, stands as a renowned architectural sophisticate.

Activities
In addition to the sailing vessel *Adventure,* there are a variety of films about Charles Towne Landing and the surrounding area.

Admission
Entry fee. Open daily, 9 A.M.–5 P.M., year-round. Closed Christmas Eve and Christmas.

MT. PLEASANT
Patriots Point Naval and Maritime Museum

Patriots Point Naval
and Maritime Museum
P.O. Box 986
Mt. Pleasant, SC 29465
(803) 884-2727

Location
The museum is located in Mt. Pleasant, across the Cooper River from Charleston on Rte. 17 north. Stay to the right at the foot of the bridge and turn right at the traffic light.

Highlights
The USS *Clamagore* (submarine)
The USS *Laffey* (destroyer)
The USS *Yorktown* (aircraft carrier)
The USCGC *Comanche* (Coast Guard cutter)
The USCGC *Ingham* (Coast Guard cutter)
The NS *Savannah* (merchant ship)

The *Savannah* is a nuclear-powered U.S. freighter launched in 1959. The 585-foot vessel has a capacity of 9,500 tons, a crew of 100, and space for 60 passengers. Propelled by 20,000-horsepower turbines at a maximum speed of 20.5 knots, the *Savannah* could cruise 300,000 nautical miles on one nuclear-reactor fueling. She was a technical success but did not make money for her owners. Now, she is a part of the Patriots Point Naval and Maritime Museum at Mt. Pleasant in Charleston, South Carolina.

General Information

Patriots Point Naval and Maritime Museum, founded in 1973, is dominated by the USS *Yorktown,* a retired aircraft carrier that served in World War II, Korea, and Vietnam. Near the end of World War II "The Fighting Lady," a film depicting life on an aircraft carrier, was shot aboard the *Yorktown,* and the ship carried that nickname thereafter. Visitors may tour the ship's bridge, wheelhouse, chapel, sickbay, and other areas. Nine carrier aircraft are on display. Special exhibits include a mine collection, a shipbuilding and repair display, and artifacts from several other noted carriers. The ship's theater regularly shows "The Fighting Lady."

Also at Patriots Point are: the nuclear merchant ship *Savannah,* an experimental alternative to oil-burning cargo ships; the World

War II submarine *Clamagore,* which operated in the Atlantic and the Mediterranean and patrolled Cuban waters during 1962; the destroyer *Laffey,* which participated in the D-day landings of the Allied troops at Normandy before being transferred to the Pacific; and two Coast Guard cutters—*Comanche* and *Ingham.*

Activities
Films, concerts, Boy/Girl Scout camping aboard the *Yorktown,* and a golf course

Admission
Entry fee. All vessels may be toured daily, 9 A.M.–5 P.M., 1 April–31 October; 9 A.M.–6 P.M., the rest of the year.

GEORGIA

ATHENS
U.S. Navy Supply Corps Museum

U.S. Navy Supply Corps Museum
U.S. Navy Supply Corp School
Prince Avenue and Oglethorpe Street
Athens, GA 30606-5000
(404) 354-7349 or 588-7349

Location
Take I-85 northeast from Atlanta twenty-two miles to the junction of SR-316. Head east on it the thirteen miles to Dacula, where you'll bear east on Rte. 29 the twenty-eight miles to Athens.

Highlights
Ship models
Paintings
Garden area with gazebo, fountains, seasonal plantings
Library and archives
Gift shop/catalog sales

General Information
The U.S. Navy Supply Corps Museum, founded in 1974, is housed in the 1910 Carnegie Library of the former State Normal School/Teacher's College.

The museum maintains a substantial holding of photos, official records, ledgers, yearbooks, and miscellaneous documents pertaining to the history of the corps and the men and women who have been a part of it. Collections include uniforms, shipboard equipment, models, paintings, and personal memorabilia.

Facilities also include a library and archives related to U.S. Navy supply operations.

Activities
Guided tours, and library/archives available for research by appointment

Admission
No entry fee. Open Monday–Friday, 8:30 A.M.–5 P.M., year-round. Closed national holidays.

ATLANTA
HMS *Bounty* Exhibit

HMS *Bounty* Exhibit
One CNN Center, Suite 275
Atlanta, GA 30303-2705
(404) 827-2491

Location
HMS *Bounty* cruises to domestic and international ports annually. Contact the above address for port-to-port information.

Highlights
HMS *Bounty*
Costumed actors and musicians serve as crew, guides, and entertainers.

General Information
HMS *Bounty* is a full-size re-creation built in Nova Scotia for MGM's 1962 film "Mutiny on the *Bounty*." The ship is equipped with eighteenth-century nautical furnishings, and tour guides are on hand to give historical information about that era and the mutiny.

The original *Bounty* was a coastal trader named *Bethia*. The navy of King George III selected her over five other vessels as admirably suited for Bligh's mission to the South Seas. She was bought for £1,950 and taken into the shipyards of Deptford on the River Thames for full conversion. There she was armed with four four-pounder carriage guns and ten half-pounder swivels.

Because of the munificent nature of her mission—to collect young transplants of the breadfruit tree and carry them to Jamaica for cultivation as a cheap food for slaves—she was rechristened the *Bounty*.

Activities
Available for private parties, fundraising-event sponsorship, demonstrations, and educational venues.

Admission
Entry fee. Open daily, 11 A.M.–6 P.M., depending on port stays.

COLUMBUS
Confederate Naval Museum

Confederate Naval Museum
202 4th Street
P.O. Box 1022
Columbus, GA 31902
(404) 327-9798

Location
Columbus is on the Chattahoochee River in western Georgia. Follow I-85 south from Atlanta to the I-185 exit. Continue south on it into Columbus. The museum is just east of the Chattahoochee River Bridge at the junction of Rtes. 27, 80, and 280.

Highlights
Ship models
Gift shop

General Information
Founded in 1962, the Confederate Naval Museum is a repository that depicts the history of the Confederate States Navy (constituted 21 February 1861 under the direction of Secretary Stephen R. Mallory) and its efforts to become an important naval power that would not be outclassed by the larger, superior, established Federal Navy.

The museum's prime exhibits are the remains of two Confederate warships: the ironclad ram *Jackson* (formerly *Muscogee*) and the gunboat *Chattahoochee,* salvaged from the river near Columbus in the early 1960s. Also on display are many ship models, weapons, relics, and other exhibits relating to Confederate naval history.

Activities
Guided tours

Admission
No entry fee, but donations accepted. Open Tuesday–Saturday, 10 A.M.–5 P.M., Sunday, 2 P.M.–5 P.M., year-round. Closed Thanksgiving and Christmas.

ST. SIMONS ISLAND
Museum of Coastal History

Museum of Coastal History
101 12th Street
P.O. Box 1136
St. Simons Island, GA 31522
(912) 638-4666

Location
St. Simons Island is a town on the southern tip of the island of the same name, 7.8 miles east of Brunswick.

Highlights
Lighthouse

General Information
The Museum of Coastal History, founded in 1965 and operated by the Coastal Georgia Historical Society, is located in the restored house (built in 1872) of the lighthouse keeper. Changing exhibits depict the island's history, and the adjacent lighthouse offers a fine view of the island.

In 1737 General James Oglethorpe built Fort St. Simons as a defense against Spanish invaders from Florida. America's shipping industry led to the site's next historic role. James Gould began building a seventy-five foot lighthouse in 1807. Completed in 1810, the octagonal tower tapered from its twenty-five-foot base to a ten-foot diameter at the top.

The first lighthouse was destroyed by Confederate troops during the Civil War to prevent the beacon from aiding an invasion of the island. Rebuilt in 1872, the lighthouse has been in operation ever since, thanks perhaps to its resident ghost. Many have supposedly heard the former keeper running up and down the stairs during stormy nights, checking the lamp.

Activities
Open for tours. A climb to the top of the lighthouse, whose light beams eighteen miles to Brunswick Harbor, offers a sweeping panorama.

Admission
Entry fee. Open Tuesday–Saturday, 10 A.M.–5 P.M., Sunday, 1:30 P.M.–5 P.M., year-round. Closed Thanksgiving, Christmas Eve, Christmas, New Year's Day, and Easter.

SAVANNAH
Old Fort Jackson

Old Fort Jackson
1 Ft. Jackson Road
Savannah, GA 31404
(912) 232-3945

Location
Ft. Jackson is three miles east of Savannah. Take Islands Expressway to President Street to Woodcock Road.

Highlights
The CSS *Georgia*
Coastal water research project
Now and Then (newsletter)

General Information
Old Fort Jackson, founded in 1976, is the oldest standing fort in Georgia. It was built on Salter's Island, the site of an earlier fort and colonial brickyard. The cannons on Salter's Island were manned by four garrisons of soldiers during times of revolution, civil war, foreign invasion, martial law, and epidemic disease. The height of the fort's military use was as the Confederate headquarters of the river batteries.

The fort's collection includes cannons, small arms, tools, and machinery that are demonstrated and employed during many special events held each year.

The CSS *Georgia,* a rail ironclad, was located by dive teams from the U.S. Army Corps of Engineers and the Cultural Resources Laboratory at Texas A & M. Because of the "black water," resulting in zero visibility, the divers had to "feel" the wreckage to determine the exact location of its features and the extent of damage she had sustained through the years. During the course of diving some artifacts were recovered and are now displayed in the museum. Well worth seeing!

For two hundred years the maritime history of the south Atlantic coast has been hidden from view. Today, the Coast Heritage Society is undertaking a project to uncover this resource. A research project was begun in 1980 to locate information about small boats used in this area by our ancestors. Results of this study were published in 1982 in *Tide Craft: The Boats of Lower South Carolina and Georgia.*

Activities
(*See:* Museum of Coastal History, St. Simons Island, Georgia)

Admission
Entry fee. Open Tuesday–Sunday, 9 A.M.–5 P.M., year-round.

Ships of the Sea Maritime Museum

Ships of the Sea Maritime Museum
503 East River Street
Savannah, GA 31401
(912) 232-1511

Location
Take I-10 into the center of Savannah. The museum is a mere 100 feet from the Savannah River on East River Drive (several blocks east of City Hall).

Highlights
Ship models
Figureheads
Chandlery
Ships-in-a-bottle collection
Scrimshaw

General Information
Ships of the Sea Maritime Museum, founded in 1966, is in an 1898 restored cotton warehouse on Savannah's historic riverfront. The museum is dedicated to the great ships of the world and the brave men who sailed them. Here—just steps away from the bustling Savannah River trade of today—you'll find an outstanding collection of famous vessels spanning 2,000 years of seafaring. Ship models, scrimshaw, paintings, and maritime artifacts are displayed. Collections also include figureheads, ships' chandlery, nineteenth-century English tavern signs, macrame, and more.

Activities
Guided tours, and maritime classes for children

Admission
Entry fee. Open daily, 10 A.M.–5 P.M., year-round. Closed Christmas Eve, Christmas, and New Year's Day.

TYBEE ISLAND
The Tybee Lighthouse

Tybee Island Historical Society
Ft. Screven
P.O. Box 366
Tybee Island, GA 31328
(912) 786-5848

Location
Tybee Island lies eighteen miles east of Savannah on Rte. 80.

Highlights
Lighthouse history

General Information
"From Rabun Gap to Tybee Light" is a phrase employed by nineteenth-century Georgian politicians to measure the great expanse of the state from the north to the south. Today, it signifies the importance of the Tybee Lighthouse, which marks the mouth of the Savannah River. It is the nation's oldest active lighthouse. Built in 1773 and reconstructed after the Civil War, Tybee Light is 154 feet tall. Visitors may climb the lighthouse for a breathtaking view of Fort Screven and Tybee Island.

A small museum is housed in the 1881 keeper's cottage. A restored 1812 kitchen is open as an exhibition area. The Tybee Museum (founded in 1960) is housed in Battery Garden, a Spanish-American War coastal defense battery, and contains exhibits on coastal defense, the Martello tower, the Tybee train, the North gun collection, and the Erichsen doll collection.

Activities
Tours and lectures

Admission
Entry fee. Memberships are available. Open daily, 10 A.M.–6 P.M., April–September; 1 P.M.–5 P.M., October–March.

FLORIDA

KEY WEST
Mel Fisher Maritime Heritage Society

Mel Fisher Maritime Heritage Society
200 Greene Street
Key West, FL 33040
(305) 294-2336

Location
Key West is at the southernmost tip of Rte. 1, 156 miles south of Miami.

Highlights
Gold, silver, and jewels recovered from a Spanish galleon
Newsletter
Laboratory
Research library

General Information
The history of shipwrecks begins with those unknown mariners who first ventured out onto the uncharted sea, and for millennia the sea has guarded their secrets. Today, shipwreck archaeologists recover more and more of this priceless heritage every year.

The Mel Fisher Maritime Heritage Society, founded in 1982, displays gold jewelry, silver coins, and numerous artifacts recovered from the wreckage of the Spanish galleons *Atocha* and *Santa Margarita*. The two vessels sank forty miles off Key West in a hurricane on 6 September 1622 on their return voyages to Spain from Havana, Cuba. Exhibits detailing techniques of underwater archaeology are also displayed.

The *Atocha* yielded 906 silver bars, 115 gold bars (weighing more than 250 pounds), 60 gold coins, 750 pieces of silverware, and over 130,000 silver coins. Twelve cannons were also found, including one given to the King of Spain, Juan Carlos, in 1976 at the museum's exhibit in the great hall at the National Geographic building in Washington, D.C.

Activities
A theater, plus preservation, archaeological, and numismatic research

Admission
Entry fee. Memberships are available. Open daily, 10 A.M.–5:15 P.M., year-round.

Lighthouse Museum

Lighthouse Museum
938 White Head Street
Key West, FL 33040
(305) 294-0012

Location
Key West is on the southernmost tip of Rte. 1, 156 miles south of Miami.

Highlights
Lighthouse

General Information
The Lighthouse Museum is housed in the former lightkeeper's cabin. It contains items of history from Key West's long associa-

tion with naval activities. A display on Floridian lighthouse history is also in the garden. A grand view of the area can be obtained by climbing the lighthouse's interior spiral staircase. The tower was the first lighthouse restoration completed in the lighthouse bicentennial year (1989). The keeper's house (the museum) will be restored to its 1915 condition.

Admission
Entry fee. Open daily, 9:30 A.M.–5 P.M., year-round. Closed Christmas.

PONCE INLET
Ponce de Leon Inlet Lighthouse

Ponce De Leon Inlet Lighthouse
4931 South Peninsula Drive
Ponce Inlet, FL 32127
(904) 761-1821

Location
The inlet is just south of Daytona Beach on the Atlantic Ocean. The lighthouse is west of Atlantic Avenue on South Peninsula Drive (off Rte. 1 and I-95).

Highlights
The *F. D. Russell* (tugboat)
Quarterly newsletter
Lighthouse ship's store

General Information
Night after night from 1887 to 1970 this tall sentinel of brick and granite flashed its faithful warning "to the men who go down to the sea in ships." The lighthouse was started with the purchase of ten acres of land on 21 March 1883 and was completed in 1886.

Ponce de Leon Inlet Lighthouse museum was founded in 1972 and is in the restored 175-foot high structure. The light was reactivated by the Coast Guard in 1982.

In addition to the lighthouse there are three other buildings: 1. The 2nd assistant keeper's cottage, housing the original lens and other artifacts that document the background of Ponce de Leon Inlet; 2. The head lightkeeper's house, operating as a sea museum; and 3. the 1st assistant keeper's cottage, named after Gladys Meyer Davis, a life-long resident of the area whose father was the last head keeper.

Activities
Guided tours and lectures

Admission
Entry fee. Open daily, 10 A.M.–4 P.M., the day after Labor Day–30 April; 10 A.M.–7 P.M., 1 May–Labor Day.

TALLAHASSEE
Museum of Florida History

Museum of Florida History
R. A. Gray Building
500 South Bronough
Tallahassee, FL 32399-0250
(904) 488-1484

Location
Take I-10 into Tallahassee, then bear south on Rte. 27 to center city. The museum is downtown near the State Capitol.

Highlights
Florida waterways exhibit
Gift shop

General Information
The Museum of Florida History was established to promote and encourage knowledge and appreciation of the maritime history of Florida and to preserve and exhibit artifacts that relate to the history of the state.

A major new exhibit, "Waterways: The History of Water Transportation in Florida," will touch on the entire story of water transportation in Florida, with a main focus on the "golden era of steamboating." To house the exhibit, the forward quarter of the

Hiawatha, a steamboat that traveled the St. John's-Ocklawaha Rivers run to Silver Springs from 1904–20, has been converted into a museum.

Activities
Audiovisual presentations and quilting workshops

Admission
Contact the museum for information concerning opening hours.

FOUR

GULF COAST

ALABAMA

GULF SHORES
Fort Morgan Museum

Fort Morgan Museum
51 Route 180 West
Gulf Shores, AL 36542
(205) 540-7125

Location
From Mobile take I-10 east across the Mobile Bay to the Rte. 59 south exit to Gulf Shores. Or, for another point of reference, Gulf Shores lies on the Gulf of Mexico intercoastal waterway thirty miles west of Pensacola, Florida.

Highlights
Fresnel lighthouse lenses
Gift shop

General Information
Fort Morgan Museum, founded in 1967, is built on a Civil War site. The museum contains Fresnel lenses from two local lighthouses—Sand Island (from the 1870s) and Mobile Point (from the 1850s). The museum also contains lightkeepers' uniforms and memorabilia.

Admission
Entry fee. Open Monday–Friday, 8 A.M.–5 P.M., Saturdays and Sundays, 9 A.M.–5 P.M., year-round. Closed Christmas and New Year's Day.

MOBILE
USS *Alabama* Battleship Memorial Park

USS *Alabama* Battleship Memorial Park
P.O. Box 65
Mobile, AL 36601
(205) 433-2703

Location
From Mobile take I-10 east for approximately 1.5 miles to the Battleship Parkway exit. The park is at the head of Mobile Bay just off the Gulf of Mexico.

Highlights
The USS *Alabama* (BB 60) (battleship)
The USS *Drum* (SS 228) (submarine)

General Information
The USS *Alabama* Battleship Memorial Park, founded in 1963, is a seventy-five-acre park dedicated to Alabama's war veterans. The park's two main attractions are the USS *Alabama* (1942) and the submarine USS *Drum* (1941), both participants in many World War II sea battles. The park complex also features military aircraft, including a B-52.

Most of the *Alabama*'s nine battle stars were earned while serving with a strike force in the Pacific, notably in Okinawa and Japan. The vessel's gallant military career was highlighted by its dominant role close to the end of the war. The battleship was decommissioned in 1947 and was towed 5,600 miles from Seattle, Washington, to Mobile, Alabama, where she was established as a floating shrine in 1965. The submarine USS *Drum,* docked alongside the battleship, conducted thirteen war missions in the Pacific.

Visitors may tour the *Alabama*'s decks, turrets, mess, berthing compartments, bridge, wardroom, and captain's cabin. Visitors to the USS *Drum* may go into the torpedo rooms and the crew's quarters.

Admission
Entry fee. Open daily, 8 A.M.–sunset, year-round. Closed Christmas.

MISSISSIPPI

BILOXI
Seafood Industry Museum

Seafood Industry Museum
P.O. Box 1907
Biloxi, MS 39533
(601) 435-6320

Location
From Mobile, Alabama, take I-10 southwest to exit 46 (I-110). Follow it south to Rte. 90 in Ocean Springs. Head east two miles, watching for museum signs. Through the gates into Point Cadet Plaza, the museum is on the right.

Highlights
The *Glenn L. Swetman* (schooner)
Coastal geology
Seafood industry workboats
The *Mains'l* (newsletter)

General Information
The Seafood Industry Museum was founded in 1983 and opened March 1986 in a renovated Coast Guard barracks. The museum contains a wide variety of exhibits that include: ''Coastal Geology,'' explaining the development of the Mississippi Gulf Coast over a period of 100 years; ''Biloxi's Early Fishermen and Colonial Dreams,'' describing the reasons for settlement during the period of 1699–1810; ''Seafood Capital of the World,'' explaining the development of the fishing industry from 1881 to 1900; and ''Boats of Biloxi,'' relating the history of working vessels. Collections contain photographs, objects, and implements that have been used during the industry's long and colorful history.

Also featured are nets for both commercial and recreational fishing and Biloxi's seafood workers, oystering, shrimping, and crabbing.

The schooner *Glenn L. Swetman* is a traditional topsail, two-masted wooden oyster schooner that was launched in 1989. She will be used to revive the great tradition of schooner racing once a second boat is completed.

Activities
The *Glenn L. Swetman* offers two-and-a-half hour, half-day, full-day, and multiple-day charters with professional captain and crew. Point Cadet Marina, Biloxi, is her home port.

Admission
Entry fee. Open Monday–Saturday, 9 A.M.–5 P.M., year-round.

VICKSBURG
USS *Cairo* Museum

USS *Cairo* Museum
Vicksburg National Military Park
3201 Clay Street
Vicksburg, MS 39180
(601) 636-0583

Location
Vicksburg lies on the Mississippi River forty-four miles west of Jackson on I-20. The museum is adjacent to Vicksburg National Cemetery.

Highlights
Library (600 volumes)

General Information
The USS *Cairo* Museum, founded in 1980, sits opposite the national cemetery entrance, the site of the 1863 Union siege of the city of Vicksburg. It displays artifacts recovered from the Union ironclad *Cairo*, which was sunk in the Yazoo River north of Vicksburg in 1862. The vessel is believed to have been the first sunk by an electrically detonated mine. A six-minute audiovisual program explains the salvage of the gunboat, which has been partially restored next to the museum. The library contains official records of the Union and Confederate armies and navies.

Activities
Self-guided tours, lectures, films, and audiovisual and education programs

Admission
Entry fee. Open daily, 8:30 A.M.–5:30 P.M., winters only. Closed Christmas

LOUISIANA

BATON ROUGE
Louisiana Naval War Memorial
USS *Kidd* (DD-661)

Louisiana Naval War Memorial Commission
USS *Kidd* (DD-661)
305 South River Road
Baton Rouge, LA 70802
(504) 342-1942

Location
Baton Rouge is approached on either I-10 east/west or I-110 north/south. It is eighty miles upstream from New Orleans. The war memorial is on the Mississippi River (across from the Baton Rouge Centroplex) at Government and Front Streets.

Highlights
The USS *Kidd* (DD-661) (destroyer)
P-40 fighter plane
Kidd's Compass (newsletter)
Gift shop

General Information
The State of Louisiana has a varied and colorful nautical history. Situated at the end of the Mississippi River and reaching into the Gulf of Mexico has made it a central trading area. Colonized under France and Spain, plantations lined the river, and steamboats were in constant motion. The river thus became an economic highway. The war memorial's Nautical Center is an educational facility where mankind and water, war and peace are the themes represented by permanent displays and changing exhibits. Galleries relate to seagoing vessels as well as boats that ventured upon our many rivers.

Of special note is the USS *Kidd* (DD-661), opened in 1983. She is a *Fletcher*-class World War II destroyer resting in a cradle that

The *Delta Queen,* built in sections in Glasgow, Scotland, was assembled in Stockton, California, in 1926. The 285-foot riverboat carried a crew of 75 who served up to 192 passengers per tour on California rivers until 1947. Purchased by the Greene Line, she continued her passenger service on the Ohio and Mississippi Rivers, where she is still a commanding presence. (Photo: Jerry MacMullen Library, Maritime Museum of San Diego.)

allows viewers to walk under the hull when the river is at its lowest level (in late summer). A museum complex displays radar, fire-control radar, and memorabilia from Destroyer Squadron 48. Other excellent exhibits are the Navy WAVEs' display and the mock-up combat information center. Collections include training manuals, publications, and nautical charts relating to the destroyer.

Activities
Guided tours, lectures, and shipboard overnight camping for youth groups

Admission
Entry fee. Memberships are available. Open daily, 9 A.M.–5 P.M., year-round. Closed Christmas.

PLAQUEMINE
Plaquemine Lock

Plaquemine Lock
Iberville Parish Parks
and Recreational District
P.O. Box 1060
Plaquemine, LA 70765
(504) 687-0641

Location
Take SR-1 south thirteen miles out from Baton Rouge. The Plaquemine Lock is on the Mississippi River off Main Street in the downtown area.

Highlights
A Mississippi River lock
History of the Mississippi River and its boat traffic

General Information
Plaquemine Lock was founded in 1983 and encompasses the original lock structure and lockhouse built at the turn of the century. The lockhouse now serves as a museum. The adjacent observation

tower commands a picturesque view of the lock system and the river.

The Mississippi River and its surrounding waterways have long been considered vital assets to the people and economy of Louisiana. Yet the waters have also posed serious theats of flooding to the low-lying areas of the state, so controlling the waterways became as important as the waters themselves. Eventually, Congress was petitioned by the residents of Iberville Parish to authorize funding for a lock system to control the water level between Bayou Plaquemine and the Mississippi River.

At the time the lock was completed, in 1909, it had the highest freshwater lift of any lock in the world, namely, fifty-one feet, and it functioned on a unique engineering plan that utilizes a gravity-flow principle. This was modernized at a later date by the installation of hydraulic pumps. In 1961 a larger lock began operating at Port Allen and so the Plaquemine Lock was closed after fifty-two years of service.

Admission

No entry fee. Open daily, 8 A.M.–4 P.M., year-round. Closed national holidays.

TEXAS

CORPUS CHRISTI

Corpus Christi Museum

Corpus Christi Museum
1900 North Chaparral
Corpus Christi, TX 78401
(512) 883-2862

Location
In Corpus Christi, the museum is on Ocean Drive near the Harbor Bridge (at the end of I-37).

Highlights
Shipwreck (1554) collection
Library
Gift shop

General Information
Corpus Christi Museum houses a fascinating display of artifacts salvaged from a 1554 Spanish galleon shipwrecked off the Texas coast near the present Fort Mansfield on Padre Island. The display includes an astrolabe (predecessor of the sextant), part of the keel, and the anchor. Other items will be displayed as they are recovered and brought to the museum.

Activities
Audiovisual hurricane program, and library (used only by permission)

Admission
No entry fee. Open Tuesday–Saturday, 10 A.M.–5 P.M., Sunday, 2 P.M.–5 P.M., year-round. Closed national holidays.

FREDERICKSBURG
Admiral Nimitz State Historical Park

Admiral Nimitz State Historical Park
340 East Main Street
P.O. Box 777
Fredericksburg, TX 78624
(512) 997-4379

Location
From San Antonio travel northwest on I-10 the fifty miles to Comfort. Head north on Rte. 87 twenty-two miles to Fredericksburg.

Highlights

The Museum of the Pacific War
The Japanese Garden of Peace
The History Walk of the Pacific War (featuring tanks, guns, aircraft, and other large relics)
Library and archives on Admiral Nimitz and Pacific war topics
Steamboat Hotel (contains the marine museum)
Gift shop

General Information

Admiral Nimitz State Historical Park was originally founded in 1967 in the Nimitz family business, a hotel begun in the 1850s and active until 1964. The hotel building now features three floors of exhibits detailing Admiral Nimitz's career, with special emphasis on the Pacific theater of World War II. The Museum of the Pacific War is the only museum in the country dedicated primarily to detailing that conflict from all points of view. Many hands-on and audiovisual exhibits are featured, along with a special hallway of restored rooms from the hotel's colorful past.

Collections include all types of artifacts used in the Pacific campaigns, from uniforms and small arms to tanks, artillery, and aircraft. Of special interest are the aircraft on exhibit, including the most complete Dauntless dive bomber in existence and the most complete Japanese "Val" dive bomber to survive.

A research library including a photo collection (more than 6,000 Pacific war photos) is open by appointment only.

Activities

Temporary and traveling exhibits, and an annual symposium on various Pacific war topics

Admission

Entry fee. Open daily, 8 A.M.–5 P.M., year-round.

GALVESTON
The *Elissa*

The *Elissa*
Pier 21
2016 Strand
Galveston, TX 77550
(409) 763-1877

Location
From Houston take I-45 south to Galveston on Galveston Island. The *Elissa* is docked at Pier 21 at the foot of 22nd Street.

Highlights
The *Elissa* (iron bark)

General Information
The *Elissa* is a square-rigged iron bark built in Scotland in 1877. In 1974 she was condemned to a Greek shipyard and destined for scrap until the Galveston Historical Foundation rescued and restored her to her former grandeur.

The masts of the 400-ton square-rigger tower 103 feet above the water. One of the oldest merchant ships afloat, the *Elissa* visited Galveston in 1883 and 1886. Now, a "seaworthy" exhibit for the whole family, she will be the centerpiece of the developing Texas Seaport Museum.

The Strand Visitor's Center shows a film that describes the history and restoration of the ship (the film can also be seen at the *Elissa* Dock). The ship leaves its moorings only once each year.

Admission
Entry fee. Open Monday–Friday, 10 A.M.–5 P.M., Saturday, 10 A.M.–6 P.M., and Sunday, 10 A.M.–5 P.M., year-round.

LA PORTE
Battleship *Texas* State Historical Park

Battleship *Texas* State Historical Park
3527 Battleground Road
La Porte, TX 77571
(713) 479-2411

Location
From Houston travel southeast on I-10 eighteen miles to La Porte, on Galveston Bay.

Highlights
The USS *Texas* (battleship)

General Information
The *Texas* is the last of the dreadnoughts (a battleship equipped with big guns of the same caliber as her main armament) and the only surviving naval vessel to have seen service in *both* world wars. When the USS *Texas* was commissioned in 1914, she was the most powerful weapon in the world and the most complex product of an industrial nation just beginning to become a force in global events. The *Texas* projected American pride and power over the world's oceans for thirty-two years. Her big guns brought dread to her enemies and hope to her friends in the Pacific in 1945 as she had in the North Sea in 1918.

Always a proud ship, imbued with the spirit of her namesake, the *Texas* serves today as a monument to those who built and served in her, a powerful reminder of the skill and sacrifice, hardship and courage, demanded and freely given by Americans in their country's defense. The *Texas* has undergone modification in guns, armor, and propulsion. She helped pioneer naval aviation between the wars and was kept up-to-date with advances in fire control, radio, and radar as the focus of her defense shifted to the sky. Her basic reasons for being, however, remained the same: to float the big guns of her main battery into action and to keep them firing against any enemy response.

Activities
Self-guided tours

Admission
Entry fee. Open daily, 10 A.M.–5 P.M., September–May; 10 A.M.–6 P.M., June–August. Closed Christmas.

ROCKPORT
Texas Maritime Museum

Texas Maritime Museum
1202 Navigation Circle
P.O. Box 1836
Rockport, TX 78382
(512) 729-1271

Location
The museum is located in the center of Rockport, just minutes north of Corpus Christi, bordered by SR-35 on one side and Rockport Harbor on the other.

Highlights
Ship models
''Bullwinkle,'' a scale model of an oil drilling platform
The Log Line (newsletter)
Library
Ship's store (museum shop)

General Information
The Texas Maritime Museum was founded in 1975 and expanded in 1989 into a new building. Through changing exhibits, programs, and special events, it tells the story of the evolution of Texas through its waterborne commerce and activities: early exploration of the Texas coastline; early growth of Texas ports; European and American immigration through coastal communities; Texas's brief experience as a naval power; the boom and bust in steamboat traffic on the state's rivers; offshore, inshore, and river navigation; shipbuilding; and the development of the commercial fishing industry.

Activities
Education programs

Admission
Entry fee. Open Wednesday–Saturday, 10 A.M.–5 P.M., Sunday, 12:30 P.M.–5 P.M., year-round. Closed Thanksgiving, Christmas, New Year's Day, and Easter.

FIVE

GREAT LAKES

ONTARIO, CANADA

COLLINGWOOD
Collingwood Museum

Collingwood Museum
P.O. Box 556
Collingwood, Ontario L9Y 4B2
Canada
(705) 445-4811

Location
From Toronto travel north on Rte. 400 about sixty miles to the junction of Canadian Rte. 6. Head west on it about thirty miles to Collingswood on Nottawasaga Bay. The museum is in Memorial Park on St. Paul Street.

Highlights
Nineteenth-century ship models

General Information
The Collingwood Museum, founded in 1966, is housed in a former railroad station. The museum exhibits are devoted to the community and its extensive shipbuilding activities and to Petun Indian artifacts.

Activities
Films, group tours (by appointment only). The museum's special events and programs include a "Steam Show" in June, Canada Day (July 1) festivities, and traditional Christmas celebrations.

Admission
Entry fee. Open Monday–Saturday, 10 A.M.–5 P.M., Sunday, noon–4 P.M., 24 May–Thanksgiving; Wednesday–Saturday, noon–4 P.M., the day after Thanksgiving–23 May.

HAMILTON
Hamilton-Scourge Project

Hamilton-Scourge Project
City Hall
71 Main Street West
Hamilton, Ontario L8N 3T4
Canada
(416) 526-4601

Location
Hamilton is about forty-six miles west of Niagara Falls on Lake Ontario's waterfront.

Highlights
The *Hamilton* and *Scourge* (1812 schooners still to be raised from Lake Ontario)
Gift shop

General Information
The *Hamilton-Scourge* Project, founded in 1980, relates to two armed merchant schooners from the War of 1812 that capsized on Lake Ontario in a squall on 8 August 1813. In 1973 the vessels were discovered intact and perfectly preserved in 300 feet of water, six miles off Port Dalhousie, Ontario.

Title to the vessels was transferred in 1980 to the City of Hamilton from the U.S. Navy through the U.S. Congress and the Royal Ontario Museum. It is expected that the two ships will be raised and exhibited in a world-class museum in Hamilton, Ontario. Three levels of Canadian Government—municipal, provincial, and federal—are participating in this project.

The *Hamilton-Scourge* Society is open to membership by the general public and sells related posters, books, and *National Geographic* (March 1983) limited edition prints. (Scholars are welcome to study at the project offices, Monday–Friday, 9 A.M.–5 P.M.)

Activities
Research on the two schooners, speakers bureau, exhibition program, and Visitor's Center

Admission
No entry fee. Visitor's Center open Wednesday–Sunday, noon–5 P.M., July and August.

KINGSTON
Marine Museum of the Great Lakes at Kingston

Marine Museum of the
Great Lakes at Kingston
55 Ontario Street
Kingston, Ontario K7L 1Y2
Canada
(613) 542-2261

Location
Take I-81 north out of Watertown, New York, thirty miles into Canada. At the junction of Rte. 401 bear west eight miles to Kingston. The museum is on the northeast shore of Lake Ontario near the Thousand Islands tourist area, five blocks west of Kingston City Hall.

Highlights
The *Alexander Henry* (3,000-ton icebreaker converted to a bed and breakfast)
Publications
Library and archives

General Information
The Marine Museum of the Great Lakes at Kingston, founded in 1976, focuses on shipbuilding and shipping on the Great Lakes. Four buildings along the east side of drydock (1891) include a stone building that was a powerhouse whose machinery operated the heavy drydock gate and the pumps for emptying it.

Artifacts collected by divers and the shipping industry of the Great Lakes are exhibited along with the 3,000 ton, 210-foot icebreaker *Alexander Henry*. Almost all items in the museum are related to ships, shipping, and shipbuilding.

A marine library and archival collection includes over 20,000 builders' drawings of Great Lakes ships as well as nineteenth- and twentieth-century shipping and shipbuilding records.

Activities
Annual lectures

Admission
Entry fee. Memberships are available. Open daily, 10 A.M.–5 P.M., April–October; Tuesday–Sunday, 10 A.M.–4 P.M., November–mid-December. Library and archives are open all year by appointment. Bed and breakfast operates mid-May–Labor Day.

MALLORYTOWN
St. Lawrence Islands National Park/Brown's Bay Wreck

St. Lawrence Islands National
Park/Brown's Bay Wreck
P.O. Box 469, R.R. 3
Mallorytown, Ontario K0E 1R0
Canada
(613) 923-5261

Location
Take I-81 north from Watertown, New York, to the St. Lawrence Islands National Park. The park is a collection of twenty-one islands between the cities of Kingston and Brockville. Water taxis operate from Gananoque and Rockport in Canada and from Alexandria Bay and Clayton in the United States.

Highlights
1812 gunboat (a flat-bottomed clinker-built [i.e., with overlapping planks/plates like the clapboards on a house] vessel)

General Information
"When I was a youngster we used to go skating in Brown's Bay in the winter time, and if the ice was clear of snow and the moon was full, you could see a ship frozen in the ice with its copper fasteners shining like gold." Her ribs black against the green of the river, the old wreck lay quietly in the silt and sand of Brown's Bay. Children used her as a diving platform, duck hunters built blinds on her bow, and fishermen lost many a lure to her oaken sides.

In the mid-'60s, national park staff arranged for the hulk to be raised. Because of certain markings she was thought to be a gunboat dating around 1817. Gunboats usually mounted two cannons, were powered by sail and oar, carried supplies and escorted troops, scouted the shore, and in time of hostilities, harassed larger vessels. Although hundreds were in service on the Great Lakes and the Atlantic, the Baltic, and the Mediterranean seas, the gunboats have vanished, except for a few rare hulks such as this one.

The St. Lawrence Islands National Park/Brown's Bay Wreck was founded in 1904. The gunboat went on display in 1968 in a special building and cradle at the national park headquarters.

Activities
Guided tours and a film of the raising of the gunboat

Admission
No entry fee. Open daily, 10 A.M.–5 P.M., 18 May–3 September; 11 A.M.–4:30 P.M., 4 September–8 October. Other times by appointment.

MANITOWANING
Assiginack Historical Museum and SS *Norisle* Heritage Park

Assiginack Historical Museum
and SS *Norisle* Heritage Park
c/o Municipal Clerk
Box 238
Manitowaning, Ontario P0P 1N0
Canada
(705) 859-3196

Location
Manitowaning is on the eastern side of Manitoulin Island in northern Lake Huron, about 140 miles east of Mackinaw City, Michigan. Approachable from the north via Canadian Rte. 69 to Little Current. Follow island Rte. 6 south 20 miles to Manitowaning.

Highlights
The SS *Norisle* (Great Lakes ship)

General Information
The Assiginack Historical Museum, founded in 1955, is housed in what was once a jail, built around 1857, and contains general displays of marine historical interest. Located on the same grounds are a pioneer blacksmith's shop, barn, home, and school. Manitowaning Roller Mills, built in 1885 as a gristmill, exhibits an agricultural display. The SS *Norisle* tour gives a full view of the workings of a large Great Lakes ship.

Activities
Tours during July and August, small-craft docking available adjacent to Heritage Park, and full small-craft services, shopping, and restaurants nearby

Admission
Entry fee. Open daily, 10 A.M.–5 P.M., June, July, and August; daily, 11 A.M.–4 P.M., September.

PENETANGUISHENE*
Historic Naval and Military Establishments

Historic Naval and Military Establishments
P.O. Box 1800
Penetanguishene, Ontario L0K 1P0
Canada
(705) 526-7838

Location
From Toronto, travel ninety miles northwest on Rte. 400. Exit at Craighurst onto Rte. 93 west and north to Penetanguishene.

* Pen-et-ANG-wish-een: an Abenaki Indian word meaning "place of the rolling white sands."

Highlights
The *Bee* (schooner)

General Information
The Historic Naval and Military Establishments, founded in 1971, houses a collection of reconstructed and restored buildings, a period and reproduction collection, maps and manuscripts, and a replica of the schooner *Bee*.

Activities
Guided tours, historical demonstrations and dramas, education programs, and ship displays

Admission
Entry fee. Open daily, 10 A.M.–4:15 P.M., Victoria Day (the Monday preceding 25 May) weekend–Labor Day.

PORT CARLING
Muskoka Lakes Museum

Muskoka Lakes Museum
P.O. Box 432
Port Carling, Ontario P0B 1J0
Canada
(705) 765-5367

Location
Take Rte. 400 north of Toronto approximately 138 miles to Victoria Harbor, they follow Rte. 69 to Foots Bay. Head east, then, to Port Carling on Rte. 118.

Highlights
Boatbuilding
Antique boat show

General Information
The Muskoka Lakes Museum-Port Carling was founded in 1967 and exhibits: artifacts used by early settlers in the Muskoka area from 1865; marine displays relating to the region's boatbuilders

and their boats; a local, relocated, squared-timber house (c. 1875); and photos and artifacts from early Muskoka resorts.

Activities
Antique boat show, Muskoka Art Show, construction of lapstrake (i.e., with overlapping planks/plates like the clapboards on a house) skiff, children's and school programs, workshop, and special events

Admission
Entry fee. Open daily, 10 A.M.–5 P.M., June–Thanksgiving.

PORT COLBORNE
Port Colborne Historical and Marine Museum

Port Colborne Historical and
Marine Museum
P. O. Box 572
Port Colborne, Ontario L3K 5X8
Canada
(416) 834-7604

Location
Port Colborne lies thirty-four miles directly west of Buffalo, New York, on Canadian Rte. 3.

Highlights
Welland Canal
Wheelhouse from the steam tug *Yvonne Dupre Jr.*
Arabella's Tearoom

General Information
The Port Colborne Historical and Marine Museum, founded in 1974, is housed in a Georgian revival style home built in 1869. It exhibits artifacts pertaining to the early history of this area including: the Welland Canal; a heritage village site with an 1818 log schoolhouse; a blacksmith shop circa the 1880s; a 1946 wheelhouse; a 1915 tearoom; and an 1850s loghouse.

Canal Days is held on Canada's civic holiday weekend (the first Monday in August) and features marine displays, an outdoor arts and crafts show, demonstrations, entertainment, and food.

Activities
Group tours, Canal Days, and a Christmas festival held the first weekend in December

Admission
No entry fee for the museum. Various fees for special events. Open Tuesday–Sunday, noon–5 P.M., May–December.

PORT DOVER

Port Dover Harbour Museum

Port Dover Harbour Museum
44 Harbour Street, Box 1298
Port Dover, Ontario N0A 1N0
Canada
(519) 583-1526 or 585-2660

Location
Port Dover lies approximately seventy-two miles southwest of Niagara Falls on Lake Erie. Take Rte. 3 to Jarvis, then Rte. 6 south the thirteen miles to Port Dover.

Highlights
Schooner trade history
Freshwater commercial fishing history

General Information
Founded in 1976, the Port Dover Harbour Museum exhibits artifacts and photos relating to schooner trade and fishing on the north shore of Lake Erie.

Activities
Research facilities and slide shows

Admission
No entry fee, but donations accepted. Open daily, 10 A.M.–5:30 P.M., 15 May–the second Monday in October (Canadian Thanksgiving).

ST. CATHARINES
St. Catharines Historical Museum

St. Catharines Historical Museum
1932 Canal Road
P.O. Box 3012
St. Catharines, Ontario L2R 7C2
Canada
(416) 984-8880

Location
St. Catharines is only ten miles west of Niagara Falls off Rte. 58 (north from Rte. 3).

Highlights
Welland Canal
Library and archives
Photograph collection

General Information
The St. Catharines Historical Museum was founded in 1965 and opened in 1967. It has a collection of agricultural and industrial implements; pioneer and household furnishings and utensils; workmen's handtools; firefighting equipment; marine and canal artifacts; china, glass, and crockery; military artifacts; ethnic arts and crafts; maps and plans; and manuscript material.

Certain galleries display and feature the historical development of the four Welland Canals. Other galleries feature artists and artisans, health spas and mineral springs, the local militia, commerce, and firefighting equipment (including an early steam-operated waterpump).

Activities
Lectures, special annual events, guided tours, educational programs, audiovisual presentations, research facilities, library, and archives

Admission
Entry fee. Open Monday–Friday, 9 A.M.–5 P.M., Saturdays, Sundays, and holidays, 1 P.M.–5 P.M., year-round. Closed Christmas, the day after Christmas, New Year's Day, and Good Friday.

SAULT STE. MARIE
Museum Ship *Norgoma*

Museum Ship *Norgoma*
St. Mary's River Marine Center
P.O. Box 325
Sault Ste. Marie, Ontario P6A 5L8
Canada
(705) 942-6984

Location
Sault Ste. Marie lies on the Canadian-Michigan border where Lakes Huron and Superior meet. The twin cities are about 175 miles west of Sudbury on Canadian Rte. 178.

Highlights
The *Norgoma* (Great Lakes cruise ship)

General Information
The Museum Ship *Norgoma,* founded in 1976, exhibits this 188-foot diesel-powered passenger vessel (built in 1950), featuring historical artifacts on her main deck. The *Norgoma* was the last overnight cruise ship built on the Great Lakes. She ran from Owen Sound to Sault Ste. Marie between 1950 and 1963, after which she served as an auto ferry to Manitoulin Island until 1974.

Activities
Entire ship open for touring

Admission
Entry fee. Open daily, 10 A.M.–6 P.M., June; 9 A.M.–9 P.M., July–August; 10 A.M.–6 P.M., September.

SOUTH BAY
Mariners' Park Museum

Mariners' Park Museum
c/o Mrs. B. Van Dusen
R.R. 2
Milford, Ontario K0K 2P0
Canada
(613) 476-3972

Location
South Bay is approximately 100 miles east of Toronto near Belleville. Take Rte. 49 south from Rte. 401 the 10 miles to Rte. 17. Follow it 10 miles farther to Milford, turning onto Rte. 9 for 1 mile to South Bay on Lake Ontario.

Highlights
Artifacts from the *Protostatis, Sheboygan,* and *Acadian* (lake freighters)

General Information
The Mariners' Park Museum, founded in 1967, exhibits artifacts from the Great Lakes and surrounding waters. These include a lifeboat from the Greek freighter *Protostatis,* an anchor from the *Sheboygan,* and a wheelhouse from the *Acadian.*

Activities
Tours by appointments, Mariners' outdoor church service held annually on the second Sunday in August

Admission
Entry fee. Open Saturdays and Sundays, 10 A.M.–5 P.M., 24 May–1 July; daily, 10 A.M.–5 P.M., 2 July–30 September; Saturdays and Sundays, 10 A.M.–5 P.M., 1 October–Thanksgiving. Closed during the winter.

TORONTO

HMCS *Haida*

HMCS *Haida*
Ontario Place Corporation
955 Lakeshore Boulevard West
Toronto, Ontario M6K 3B9
Canada
(416) 956-6331

Location
In Toronto, the *Haida* is permanently berthed at Ontario Place on Lakeshore Boulevard West.

Highlights
Noon-day gun salutes daily

General Information
The HMCS *Haida* served in World War II and the Korean War. The museum, founded in 1965, exhibits a collection housed in a Royal Canadian Navy destroyer and serves as a naval memorial and maritime museum.

Activities
Self-conducted tours, with guides stationed at points throughout the ship to answer questions. (Special tours for school groups by appointment.)

Admission
Entry fee. Open daily, 10 A.M.–7 P.M., mid-May–Labor Day.

Marine Museum of Upper Canada

Marine Museum of Upper Canada
c/o Toronto Historical Board
Exhibition Place
Toronto, Ontario M6K 3C3
Canada
(416) 392-6827

Location

The museum is located at Exhibition Place, just west of downtown Toronto at the Stanley Barracks (west of the Prince's Gates entrance).

Highlights

The *Ned Hanlan* (tugboat)

General Information

Founded in 1959, the Marine Museum of Upper Canada contains exhibits that depict the waterways of central Canada and the Great Lakes–St. Lawrence water transportation system. Housed in the magnificent 1841 Officers' Quarters of Stanley Barracks, the museum presents two floors of exhibits plus the restored 1932 steam tug *Ned Hanlan* (eighty feet), preserved in dry berth.

Additionally, the museum displays a twelve-foot tall marine triple-expansion steam engine and an exhibit on the role of inland waterways in history, featuring dugouts to modern-day lakers, fur trade artifacts, and shipping memorabilia from the days of paddle, sail, and steam.

The *Dauntless* (c. 1910–1914) operated as an excursion boat. She is typical of lake and river transportation on the Great Lakes and rivers. (Photo: Jerry MacMullen Library, Maritime Museum of San Diego.)

Activities
Guided tours, lectures, and special programs; English tea (afternoons only).

Admission
Entry fee. Open Monday–Saturday, 9:30 A.M.–5 P.M., Sundays and holidays, noon–5 P.M., year-round. Closed Christmas, Boxing Day (the first weekday after Christmas), New Year's Day, and Good Friday.

MICHIGAN

COPPER HARBOR
Copper Harbor Lighthouse Museum

Copper Harbor Lighthouse Museum
c/o Fort Wilkins Historic Complex
Copper Harbor, MI 49918
(906) 289-4410

Location
Copper Harbor is on Michigan's northernmost peninsula (Keweenaw) jutting into Lake Superior. Bear north on Rte. 41 at Covington (fifty-four miles west of Marquette). The lighthouse is accessible only by boat from Copper Harbor Marina.

Highlights
Lighthouse
Great Lakes shipping displays

General Information
Copper Harbor Lighthouse Museum, founded in 1866, is accessible only by a twenty-minute ride aboard the *Star of Keweenaw*. The lighthouse museum displays period settings and depicts the maritime history of Lake Superior.

Activities
One-hour lighthouse tour, hiking trails on fifteen-acre peninsula

Admission
Entry fee. Open daily, 10 A.M.–5 P.M., mid-June–Labor Day (weather permitting). Tour begins and ends at Copper Harbor Marina.

DETROIT
Detroit Historical Museum

Detroit Historical Museum
5401 Woodward Avenue
Detroit, MI 48202
(313) 833-1805

Location
In Detroit, get off I-75 at the Warren Avenue exit. The museum is located on Woodward Avenue, north of Warren Avenue and just west of I-75.

Highlights
Great Lakes maritime history
Library (1,500 volumes)
Gift shop

General Information
Founded in 1928, the Detroit Historical Museum contains collections about Detroit and Michigan that relate to social, cultural, urban, industrial, military, and Great Lakes maritime history. The library collection focuses primarily on Detroit's and Michigan's history, with only limited information on Great Lakes maritime history.

Activities
Lectures and related activities

Admission
No entry fee. Memberships are available. Open Wednesday–Sunday, 9:30 A.M.–5 P.M., year-round. Closed national holidays.

Dossin Great Lakes Museum
(*See also:* Detroit Historical Museum)

Dossin Great Lakes Museum
100 Strand/Belle Isle
Detroit, MI 48207
(313) 267-6440

Location
In Detroit go south across the Douglas MacArthur Bridge. The museum is on the south side of Belle Isle, east of downtown Detroit.

Highlights
Pilothouse from the *William Clay Ford*
Topographical model of the Great Lakes
Ship-to-shore wireless station
Submarine periscope
Ship models
Telescope (bi-monthly magazine)
Library (700 volumes)

General Information
Dossin Great Lakes Museum, founded in 1948, has a special magic and appeal that attracts thousands of visitors each year. This is where Detroit's and Michigan's maritime heritage comes alive, the place where imaginations are stirred by reminders of storm-tossed seas, sturdy sailors, and ships and men that were lost in the freshwater fury of the Great Lakes. It is the place where visitors of any age can feel a surge of nostalgia when they look at the paintings and models and artifacts that recall the fleet of magnificent sidewheelers that once steamed up and down rivers and dominated waterfronts like a flotilla of waterborne palaces.

The Dossin Great Lakes Museum is actively involved with displays, events, and activities that highlight the history of the Great Lakes. It works with such interested groups as the Great Lakes Maritime Institute, the Detroit Historical Society, the Mariner's Church of Detroit, the Greater Michigan Boat and Fishing Show, and the American Powerboat Association to stimulate interest in its lore of the lakes.

Activities
Guided tours, lectures, and films

Admission
No entry fee. Open Wednesday–Sunday, 10 A.M.–5:45 P.M., year-round. Closed national holidays.

DOUGLAS
Steamship *Keewatin*

Steamship *Keewatin*
Harbour Village
Union Street and Blue Star Highway
P.O. Box 511
Douglas, MI 49406
(616) 857-2151/2107

Location
Take I-196/Rte. 31 thirty-six miles southwest of Grand Rapids to Douglas. The *Keewatin* is moored off County Route A-2, south of the Saugatuck-Douglas Bridge.

Highlights
The *Keewatin* (steamship)

General Information
The museum, founded in 1965, is the proud owner of a former 1907 Great Lakes passenger steamship built by the Fairfield Shipbuilding and Engineering Co., Ltd., Govan, Glasgow, Scotland, for the Canadian Pacific Railroad.

Collections include old photos of the Saugatuck area, logbooks, and articles and books on the ships of the Great Lakes.

Activities
Guided tours on the 350-foot coal-burning vessel, cruises, private charters, and fishing excursions

Admission
Entry fee. Open daily, 10 A.M.–4:30 P.M., Memorial Day–Labor Day.

EMPIRE
Sleeping Bear Point Coast Guard Station Maritime Museum

Sleeping Bear Point Coast Guard
Station Maritime Museum
9922 Front Street (Rte. M-72)
P.O. Box 277
Empire, MI 49630
(616) 326-5134

Location
From Detroit take I-75 northwest the 212 miles to Grayling. Exit west onto SR-72, traveling the 75 miles to Empire on the Lake Michigan shore.

Highlights
Ship's pilothouse
Lifesaving Service information
Library (150 volumes)

General Information
Sleeping Bear Point Coast Guard Station Maritime Museum, founded in 1984, is a museum of the U.S. Lifesaving Service and the U.S. Coast Guard. Exhibits show how both have played, and continue to play, an important humanitarian role in saving lives and rescuing passengers and crews from ships in trouble in the stormy waters off the Sleeping Bear Dunes and Manitou Islands.

The dynamic story of their services is told at the maritime museum located in the restored Coast Guard Station. A completely restored and equipped boathouse contains all the rescue equipment—surfboats, line-throwing cannon, etc.—a 1910 lifesaver would have needed to make a rescue. The main museum building, housed in the old station residence, contains many interesting exhibits on the area's maritime history. A full-size mock-up of a ship's pilothouse and a restored Lifesaving Service crewman's bunkroom can be visited.

Activities
Guided tours, lectures, films, and education programs

Admission
No entry fee. Open Monday–Friday, 1 P.M.–4:30 P.M., Saturdays and Sundays, 10:30 A.M.–sunset, mid-May–30 June; daily, 10 A.M.–5 P.M., July–August; Monday–Friday, 1 P.M.–4:30 P.M., Saturdays and Sundays, 10:30 A.M.–5 P.M., 1 September–mid-October. Closed mid-October–mid-May.

FRANKFORT

Northwest Michigan Maritime Museum

Northwest Michigan Maritime Museum
413 Main Street
P.O. Box 389
Frankfort, MI 49635
(616) 352-7260

Location
Frankfort lies in northwest Michigan about thirty-nine miles southwest of Traverse City on Crystal Inlet at Betsie Bay.

Note: The museum will relocate to neighboring Elberta, Michigan, at the two-acre Elberta Maritime Park in 1992 on the centennial of the cross-lake passenger/rail ferry service. The park will also feature the 348-foot SS *City of Milwaukee* and historic shoreside structures such as an 1887 lifesaving station.

Highlights
Underwater shipwreck display
Small-craft collection
Ship models
Gift shop

General Information
The Northwest Michigan Maritime Museum was established to share and preserve northwest Michigan's colorful maritime past and present.

Activities
Audiovisual presentations—"Schooners on the Great Lakes," "Commercial Fishing," and "Steamers and Freighters"; "Song of the Lakes" concerts and sing-a-longs; Manitou Bottomland Preserve volunteer programs; Coastwatch Program; "Interpretation through Art" program; and a harbor tour by boat.

Admission
Entry fee. Open daily, 9 A.M.–5 P.M., June–September.

MACKINAC ISLAND
Mackinac Maritime Park

Mackinac Maritime Park
Mackinac Island State Park Commission
P.O. Box 370
Mackinac Island, MI 49757
(906) 847-3328

Location
Mackinac Island is located in the Straits of Mackinac between Lakes Huron and Michigan.

Highlights
The *Welcome* (armed sloop that is now a floating museum)
Old Mackinac Point Lighthouse

General Information
The maritime park opened in 1972. Displayed throughout are buoys, bells, small boats, and anchors. Between 1973 and 1980 workmen reconstructed the armed wooden sloop *Welcome* (1775) here. This vessel is now a floating museum located at the Mackinaw City Marina.

A maritime museum is also located on the first floor of the Old Mackinac Point Lighthouse in the Maritime Park. Built in 1892, the lighthouse helped guide ships through the Straits of Mackinac until 1957. Both the keeper, his assistant, and their families lived here. Throughout its sixty-six years of operation, four keepers served the lighthouse. The building has been restored, and the museum depicts the maritime history of the straits.

Activities
Costumed guides conduct tours of *Welcome* 15 June–Labor Day. Call (616) 436-5563 for information about the tour schedule.

Admission
Entry fee includes maritime park, museum, and Michilimackinac, a reconstructed eighteenth-century fur trade village. Open daily 9 A.M.–5 P.M., 15 May–15 June; 9 A.M.–7 P.M., 16 June–Labor Day; 9 A.M.–5 P.M., the day after Labor Day–14 October.

MARQUETTE
Marquette Maritime Museum

Marquette Maritime Museum
Lakeshore Drive
P.O. Box 1096
Marquette, MI 49855
(906) 226-2006

Location
Marquette is approximately 170 miles west of Sault Ste. Marie off Rtes. 41 and M-28 on the upper peninsula of Michigan.

Highlights
The *Double Nickel Deuce* (Coast Guard vessel)
Ship models
Gift shop

General Information
The Marquette Maritime Museum was founded in 1984 to preserve and promote the maritime history of Marquette and its relation-

ship to the Great Lakes. The museum is housed in an old waterworks building and exhibits a restored dispro (disappearing propeller) boat, birchbarks, photos of sailboats, steamers, freighters, fishing boats, the Lifesaving Service, and shipwrecks. Also displayed are the house flags of Great Lake ships, along with replicas of the dockside offices of the first Marquette fishing and freight passenger companies.

Also exhibited is the forty-foot Coast Guard vessel *Double Nickel Deuce,* retired in the early 1980s after forty years of service on the Great Lakes.

Activities
Self-guided tours and video of Marquette history

Admission
Entry fee. Open Tuesday–Sunday, 11 A.M.–5 P.M., Memorial Day–30 September.

MUSKEGON
Great Lakes Naval and Maritime Museum

Great Lakes Naval and Maritime Museum
P.O. Box 1692
Muskegon, MI 49433
(616) 744-9117

Location
Muskegon is thirty-three miles northwest of Grand Rapids off I-96. The museum is located on the channel at Pere Marquette Park.

Highlights
The R/V *Rachel Carson*
The USS *Silversides* (SS 236) (restored submarine)

General Information
The Great Lakes Naval and Maritime Museum was originally founded in 1972 to save and restore the USS *Silversides.* She was commissioned into the navy just eight days after the 7 December

1941 attack on Pearl Harbor and left for the first of her fourteen war patrols on 30 April 1942.

The museum has since increased its fleet to include the R/V *Rachel Carson,* formerly the USS *Crockett* (PG 88, a 165-foot long, 250-ton naval gunboat). She was converted to a research vessel in 1977 by the U.S. Environmental Protection Agency.

Activities
Guided tours, lectures, films, radio and education programs, and overnight camping facilities for groups of twenty or more

Admission
Entry fee. Memberships are available. USS *Silversides*: open daily, 10 A.M.–6 P.M., May–September; Saturdays and Sundays only, noon–6 P.M. in April (except Easter weekend) and 10 A.M.–6 P.M. in October. Ticket booth open daily, 9:30 A.M.–5:30 P.M., year-round. Call (616) 755-1230.

PORT HURON
Museum of Arts and History

Museum of Arts and History
1115 Sixth Street
Port Huron, MI 48060
(313) 982-0891

Location
Port Huron is fifty-eight miles northeast of Detroit on I-94. The museum is one block west of Business Rte. 69 at the corner of Wall and Sixth Streets.

Highlights
Great Lakes marine lore exhibits
Ship models

General Information
Founded in 1968, the Museum of Arts and History is housed in the historic Port Huron Public Library building. Exhibits feature local history (woodlands Indians, Fort St. Joseph, Fort Gratiot,

Thomas Edison's boyhood homesite), natural history, fine arts, and decorative arts. Additional displays include a pilothouse, ship models, photographs, marine archives, and Great Lakes marine art.

The historic lightship *Huron* is scheduled for opening in mid-1990.

Activities
Lake Huron Marine Lore Society meetings featuring public programs on marine topics

Admission
No entry fee, but donations accepted. Open Wednesday–Sunday, 1 P.M.–4:30 P.M., year-round. Other times by appointment. Closed national holidays.

PORT SANILAC
Sanilac Historical Museum

Sanilac Historical Museum
228 South Ridge Street
P.O. Box 158
Port Sanilac, MI 48469
(313) 622-9946

Location
From Detroit take I-94 northeast the fifty-eight miles to Port Huron. Exit onto SR-25 north and travel the thirty-three miles to Port Sanilac on the "Thumb" of Michigan along Lake Huron. The museum is at the south entrance to Port Sanilac, west of Rte. M-25.

Highlights
Navigational instruments
Marine artifacts

General Information
Sanilac Historical Museum was founded in 1964 as a countywide institution for the study and preservation of local history. Port

Sanilac was one of the many shipping docks for lake transportation in the early 1800s. Included in the village was the Port Sanilac Lighthouse (c. 1886). The village now supports the first Harbor of Refuge for pleasure craft along the Great Lakes.

The museum depicts the days of early shipping, when passengers and freight were brought out of Detroit, and one room is devoted to marine artifacts—some from the shipwrecks along the shore.

Admission
Entry fee. Open Thursday–Sunday, 1 P.M.–4:30 P.M., mid-June–Labor Day.

SAULT STE. MARIE
Museum Ship *Valley Camp*

Sault Ste. Marie Historical Sites, Inc.
P.O. Box 1668
Sault Ste. Marie, MI 49783
(906) 632-3658

Location
Sault Ste. Marie is on Michigan's upper peninsula on I-75 (fifty-five miles north of Mackinaw City). The museum is located five blocks east of the Soo locks on the corner of Johnston and Portage.

Highlights
Great Lakes Hall of Fame
Gift shop

General Information
Museum Ship *Valley Camp* is a straight-deck 550-foot Great Lakes bulk freighter listed on the National Register. The maritime museum in holds 2 and 3 includes information on the recently discovered *Edmund Fitzgerald,* a freighter that sank in 1975 during a storm on Lake Superior, and a lifeboat recovered from her. Walk-in tours of the *Valley Camp* include the pilothouse, captain's quarters, marine museum, and an aquarium. Other maritime ex-

hibits include displays on lifeboats, a Visitor's Center, a marina, picnic areas, and St. Mary's River Front Park.

Activities
Tour of the Great Lakes freighter

Admission
Entry fee. Open daily, 10 A.M.–6 P.M., 15 May–30 June and 1 September–15 October; 9 A.M.–9 P.M., July–August.

SOUTH HAVEN
Lake Michigan Maritime Museum

Lake Michigan Maritime Museum
Dyckman at the Bridge
P.O. Box 534
South Haven, MI 49090
(616) 637-8078

Location
South Haven is 180 miles due west of Detroit on I-94. Take I-196 north at Benton Heights to the Phoenix Road exit (20) into South Haven.

Highlights
Historic restored vessels
The Ship's Lamp (newsletter)
Library (1,000 volumes)
Museum store

General Information
Lake Michigan Maritime Museum, founded in 1976, contains collections of historic restored vessels, archival materials, photos, ship and small-craft models, marine art, tools and technological implements, and personal possessions, all of which pertain to the Great Lakes regional maritime history.

The museum's center building contains an exhibit gallery and research library. Additional museum facilities include a 600-foot waterfront boardwalk, a boatbuilding workshop, a historical commercial fish tug, a U.S. Lifesaving Station crew's quarters (c. 1900), and a U.S. Coast Guard boat.

Activities
Guided tours, lectures, films, gallery talks, hobby workshops, and educational programs

Admission
Entry fee. Memberships are available. Open Tuesday–Sunday, 10 A.M.–5 P.M., May–October; Tuesday–Saturday, 10 A.M.–4 P.M., November–April.

WHITEHALL
Great Lakes Marine Museum

Great Lakes Marine Museum
6199 Murray Road
Whitehall, MI 49461
(616) 894-8265

Location
Whitehall is on the western shoreline of Michigan, nineteen miles north of Muskegon off Rte. 31A.

Highlights
White River lighthouse

General Information
The Great Lakes Marine Museum was a lighthouse built in 1875 that currently displays photographs, paintings, and various marine artifacts.

Admission
Entry fee. Open Tuesday–Friday and Sunday, 11 A.M.–5 P.M., Saturday, noon–6 P.M., June–August; Saturday, noon-6 P.M., and Sunday, 11 A.M.–5 P.M., May, September, and October.

WISCONSIN

BAYFIELD
Apostle Islands National Lakeshore

Apostle Islands National Lakeshore
Route 1, Box 4
415 West Washington
Bayfield, WI 54814
(715) 779-3397

Location
Bayfield is eighty miles east of the Duluth/Superior twin cities off Rte. 63 on SR-13.

Highlights
Island fish camp
Six lighthouses
Library (500 volumes)

General Information
Apostle Islands National Lakeshore was founded in 1970. Collections include lighthouse artifacts and objects; building and docks from small, family-run commercial fishing operations; an island fish camp; a turn-of-the-century fishing boat, and other local exhibits.

The library collection on the natural and cultural history of northern Wisconsin is available for use on the premises.

Activities
Guided tours, films, exhibits, and slide programs

Admission
No entry fee. Open daily, 8 A.M.–6 P.M., Memorial Day–Labor Day; Monday–Friday, 8 A.M.–4:30 P.M., the day after Labor Day–the day before Memorial Day.

FISH CREEK
Eagle Lighthouse

Eagle Lighthouse
Peninsula State Park
Fish Creek, WI 54212
(414) 868-3258

Location
From Green Bay take SR-57 north to Sturgeon Bay. Follow SR-42 fifty-seven miles farther north to the village of Fish Creek in Peninsula State Park.

Highlights
Lighthouse

General Information
The Eagle Lighthouse exhibits a collection of maritime and period furnishings in a historic house.

Admission
Entry fee. Open daily, 9:30 A.M.–4 P.M., June–Labor Day.

GILLS ROCK
Gills Rock Maritime Museum
(*See also:* Sturgeon Bay Marine Museum)

Gills Rock Maritime Museum
6427 Green Bay Road
Sturgeon Bay, WI 54235
(414) 743-4225

Location
Take SR-67 northeast of Green Bay to Sturgeon Bay, then follow SR-42 to Gills Rock at the extreme north end of the peninsula. The museum is at Gills Rock Memorial Park.

Highlights
Boardable fish tug

General Information
Gills Rock Maritime Museum is one of the two Door County Maritime Museums founded in 1974 on the water corridor between Green Bay and Lake Michigan. The interesting fragments and objects retrieved from these waters relate to the vast history of commercial fishing and shipbuilding in Door County. Collections also include: a boardable full-size fish tug where you see, first-hand, how gill-net fishing was done; a gill-net drying reel; several very old marine engines used in various fishing boats; and a large collection of historic marine pictures and writings.

Admission
No entry fee. Open daily, 10 A.M.–4 P.M., 23 May–7 September.

MANITOWOC

Manitowoc Maritime Museum

(*See also:* Rogers Street Fishing Museum—Two Rivers, WI)

Manitowoc Maritime Museum
75 Maritime Drive
Manitowoc, WI 54220-6823
(414) 684-0218

Location
Manitowoc is eighty-three miles north of Milwaukee on I-43. The museum is at the corner of 8th Street and Maritime Drive.

Highlights
The USS *Cobia* (submarine)
Ship models
Gift shop

General Information
One hundred years of Great Lakes maritime heritage is preserved at the Manitowoc Maritime Museum, founded in 1968 in the Manitowoc-Two Rivers area of Wisconsin. The lakeshore area, slightly over an hour north of Milwaukee, thinks of itself as Wisconsin's maritime capital. The museum is justly proud of its dis-

play of model ships and the workshop where skilled craftsmen build them. Historical information—from sailing ships to modern Great Lakes ships—is displayed along with World War II submarines and maritime treasures. It's an eye-popping adventure for the whole family.

Tied up adjacent to the museum is a national historic landmark—the USS *Cobia*, a submarine like the twenty-eight U.S. Navy subs built in Manitowoc during World War II.

Activities
Tour of the USS *Cobia*

Admission
Entry fee. Open daily, 9 A.M.–5 P.M., year-round. Closed Thanksgiving, Christmas, New Year's Day, and Easter.

STURGEON BAY

Sturgeon Bay Marine Museum

(*See also:* Gills Rock Maritime Museum)

Sturgeon Bay Maritime Museum
6427 Green Bay Road
Sturgeon Bay, WI 54235
(414) 743-4225

Location
From Milwaukee take I-43 north the 121 miles to Green Bay. Then follow SR-57 38 miles northeast to Sturgeon Bay. The museum is in Sunset Park at the site of the Roen Steamship Company.

Highlights
Small craft

General Information
Sturgeon Bay Marine Museum is housed in the historic former offices of the Roen Steamship Company. Exhibits include: the private office of Captain John Roen; a refurbished pilothouse of a Great Lakes vessel; a Kollenburg marine engine; antique outboards; and single-cylinder stationary engines used in small boats of all kinds.

Collections include a large number of marine pictures and historical papers and books that cover the marine history of the Door County area. Available for research on the premises are miscellaneous papers, pictures, and books from the shipyards and steamship operation.

Admission
No entry fee, but donations accepted. Memberships are available. Open daily, 10 A.M.–noon and 1:30 P.M.–4 P.M., 26 May–3 September.

SUPERIOR
Head of the Lakes Maritime Society

Head of the Lakes Maritime Society
P.O. Box 775
Superior, WI 54880
(715) 392-5742

Location
Superior is just south of Duluth on the Wisconsin/Minnesota state line. The society's museum is east of the downtown area off Rte. 2 and North 28th Street.

Highlights
The SS *Meteor* (whaleback ship)
Ship models
Gift shop

General Information
Head of the Lakes Maritime Society was established to inform and educate the public about the nautical and maritime heritage of Superior. It operates and promotes a museum and other related educational/informational exhibits.

Activities
Tours on the SS *Meteor* (see next entry)

Admission
Entry fee. Open daily, 10 A.M.–7 P.M., June–August; Saturdays and Sundays only, 10 A.M.–5 P.M., September–October.

SS *Meteor* Maritime Museum
(*See also:* Head of the Lakes Maritime Society)

SS *Meteor* Maritime Museum
Barker's Island
P.O. Box 775
Superior, WI 54880
(715) 392-5742/1083

Location
Superior is in the northwest corner of Wisconsin, across the mouth of the St. Louis River from Duluth, Minnesota. The ship is moored on Barker's Island.

Highlights
The SS *Meteor* (whaleback ship)
Working triple-expansion steamship engine
Ship models

General Information
The SS *Meteor* Maritime Museum, founded in 1973, is a historic museum housed in the hull and quarters of the 1896 SS *Meteor,* the last of the whalebacks. Collections include whaleback artifacts, boat models, ship equipment, shipbuilding history, gallery display, and a seamen's memorial statue, dedicated in part to the twenty-nine crewmen lost aboard the *Edmund Fitzgerald.*

Note: Duluth, Minnesota, and Superior, Wisconsin, are twin cities. The Canal Park Marine Museum and the freighter SS *William A. Irvine* in Duluth, and the SS *Meteor* Marine Museum in Superior, are only a short distance apart in Superior Bay.

Activities
Guided tours and films

Admission
Entry fee. Memberships are available. Open daily, 10 A.M.–5 P.M., Memorial Day–July; 10 A.M.–7 P.M., July–mid-August; Saturdays and Sundays, 10 A.M.–5 P.M., September–October.

TWO RIVERS
Rogers Street Fishing Museum
(*See also:* Manitowoc Maritime Museum)

Rogers Street Fishing Museum
Two Rivers, WI 54241
(715) 684-0218

Location
Two rivers is ten miles north of Manitowoc via Rte. 42, which hugs the shore of Lake Michigan.

Highlights
Tugboat
Small lighthouse

General Information
The Rogers Street Fishing Museum, on the banks of the East Twin River, tells about the city's long history as a commercial fishing

The *Queen Elizabeth,* built for the Cunard–White Star Line, was the largest passenger liner ever built (1,029 feet long). Launched 27 September 1938, she was completed in 1940 and left Clyde, England, for New York for fear that the Luftwaffe might attack her. After service as a troop transport in World War II, she served as a magnificent passenger liner. She was purchased by a Hong Kong financier to become a floating university. During refitting she caught fire and completely burned. She is now a partially sunken hulk in Hong Kong Bay.

center. A forty-foot fishing tug is on display, as well as a small lighthouse, a 5,000-pound marine diesel engine, tools, and photographs.

Admission
Call or write the Manitowoc Maritime Museum for information about opening hours.

MINNESOTA

DULUTH
Canal Park Marine Museum

Canal Park Marine Museum
Detroit District
U.S. Army Corps of Engineers
Duluth, MN 55802
(218) 727-2497

Location
In Duluth, the museum sits alongside the Duluth Ship Canal at the entrance to the Duluth-Superior harbor.

Highlights
Fore-and-aft steam engine
Ship models
The Nor'easter (newsletter)
Library

General Information
Canal Park Marine Museum was founded in 1973 by the U.S. Army Corps of Engineers. The Corps and the Lake Superior Marine Museum Association have developed a fine maritime collection, with shipwreck relics, full-size replicas of ship cabins, hard-hat diving gear, photographs, charts, marine engines, and numerous ship models. Colorful exhibits explore such subjects as the anatomy of an oreboat, Lake Superior shipwrecks, harbor dredging operations, mining, lumbering, and the grain trade.

Activities
Lively audiovisual programs, operating radar, and ship-to-shore radio keep visitors informed and interested in current harbor activity. Archival collections are also maintained at the site for use by scholars and steamboat enthusiasts.

Note: Duluth, Minnesota, and Superior, Wisconsin, are twin cities. The Canal Park Marine Museum and the freighter SS *William A. Irvine* in Duluth, and the SS *Meteor* Marine Museum in Superior, are only a short distance apart in Superior Bay.

Admission
No entry fee. Memberships are available. Open daily, 10 A.M.–9 P.M. in summer; daily, 10 A.M.–6 P.M. in spring and fall; Friday–Sunday, 10 A.M.–4:30 P.M. in winter.

MOORHEAD
Heritage *Hjemkomst* Interpretive Center

Heritage *Hjemkomst* Interpretive Center
202 1st Avenue North
Moorhead, MN 56560
(218) 233-5604

Location
From Minneapolis take I-94 northwest to Moorhead (just across from Fargo, North Dakota). Take the 8th Street North exit (Rte. 75) to the intersection of 1st Avenue North.

Highlights
The *Hjemkomst* (Viking ship reproduction)
Heritage Gift Shop

General Information
Heritage *Hjemkomst* Interpretive Center, founded in 1963, was established to create a home for the reproduction Viking ship *Hjemkomst* (pronounced YEM-komst, meaning homecoming). At the center you can see how one man made a dream come true. "A Dream Is a Dream" tells the story, from the building of this Viking ship till the end (19 July 1982) of its incredible voyage more than 6,100 miles from Duluth, Minnesota, across the Atlantic Ocean to Bergen, Norway.

Activities
Audiovisual presentations about the exhibits, a documentary (twenty-eight minutes) on *Hjemkomst*

Admission
Entry fee. Open Monday–Saturday, 9 A.M.–5 P.M.; Sunday noon–5 P.M., year-round.

TWO HARBORS
Split Rock Lighthouse Historic Site

Split Rock Lighthouse Historic Site
2010 Highway 61 East
Two Harbors, MN 55616
(218) 226-4372

Location
From Minneapolis/St. Paul travel north on I-35 to Duluth. Then head northeast on Rte. 61 about fifty-eight miles to the state park in Two Harbors.

Highlights
Split Rock Lighthouse
Fog-signal building
Restored lightkeeper's residence
Gift shop

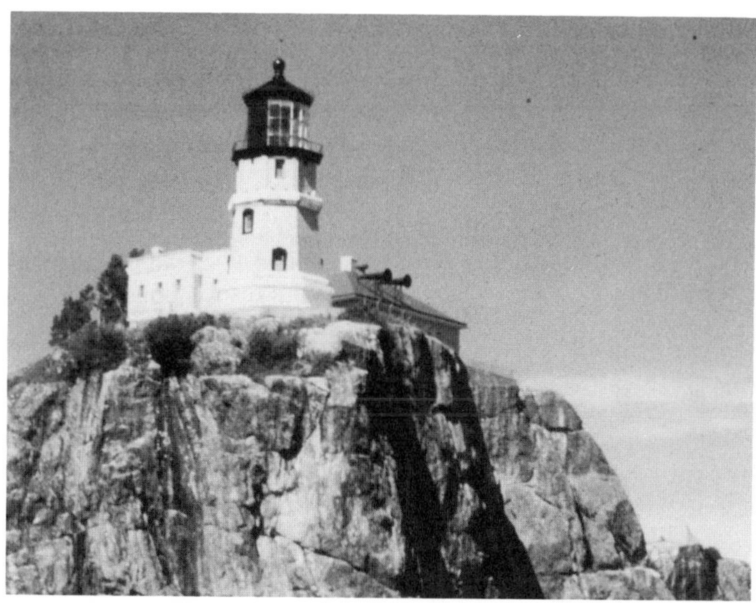

The Split Rock Lighthouse is now maintained as a historic site by the Minnesota Historical Society. Split Rock Light served as a guide to iron ore ships on western Lake Superior from 1910 to 1969. (Photo: Courtesy of Minnesota Historical Society.)

General Information

The Split Rock Lighthouse was established as a museum in 1976 and became one of Minnesota's best-known landmarks almost as soon as it opened. Today, restored to its pre-1924 appearance by the Minnesota Historical Society, it offers visitors a glimpse of lighthouse duty in the years when the isolated station could only be reached by water.

The museum exhibits artifacts pertaining to the navigational and maritime history of the Great Lakes, the iron ore industry, and commercial fishing. Visitors to the historic site may tour the lighthouse, fog-signal building, and the restored keeper's dwelling. The history center and museum shop are adjacent to the lighthouse. The center houses a ninety-seat theater that features the twenty-two-minute film "Split Rock Light: Tribute to the Age of Steel."

Activities
Documentary on Split Rock Lighthouse, guided tours of the lens and clockworks at the lighthouse, the lightkeeper's residence, and the fog-signal building

Admission
No entry fee. Open daily 9 A.M.–5 P.M., 15 May–15 October; Fridays, Saturdays, and Sundays, noon–4 P.M., 16 October–14 May. Open at other times for groups with reservations.

SIX

MID-WEST

OHIO

CANAL FULTON
Canal Fulton Heritage Society

Canal Fulton Heritage Society
103 Tuscarawas Street
P.O. Box 584
Canal Fulton, OH 44614
(216) 854-3808

Location
Canal Fulton is twelve miles south of Akron on the Tuscarawas River on County Route 93.

Highlights
The *St. Helena III* (canal freighter)
Historic Oberlin House
Old Canal Days Museum
Ohio and Erie Canal and local history
Gift shop

General Information
Since its founding in May 1968, the Canal Fulton Heritage Society has undertaken the task of advancing, encouraging, and promoting the design, development, and preservation of a historically attractive environment for the village of Canal Fulton. The society has come to operate: the *St. Helena III,* an authentically reproduced mule-drawn canal freighter; the Heritage House/Old Canal Days Museum and gift shop; and the salt-box style Oberlin House, where life during the canal days is depicted. Collections include furnishings, canal artifacts, photographs, and maps.

Activities
Canal boat and museum tours, including a slide show on the Ohio and Erie Canal, and tours of the Oberlin House. Walking tours of historic downtown also available.

Admission
Memberships are available.

Museum: entry fee. Open Tuesday–Saturday, 1 P.M.–5 P.M., June–August.

Boat rides: entry fee. Open Tuesday–Saturday, 1:30 P.M.–2:30 P.M., and 3:30 P.M., Sunday, 1:30 P.M., 2:30 P.M., 3:30 P.M., and 4:30 P.M.

Oberlin House: no entry fee. Open by appointment.

CLEVELAND
USS *Cod* Submarine Museum

USS *Cod* Submarine Museum
1089 East 9th Street
Cleveland, OH 44144
(216) 566-8770

Location
In downtown Cleveland, the museum is at the intersection of North Marginal Road and East 9th Street. It is adjacent to the U.S. Coast Guard Station at the harbor.

Highlights
The USS *Cod* (SS 224)

General Information
The USS *Cod* is the last completely authentic World War II *Gato*-class submarine, now a floating museum located on Cleveland's lakefront. The *Cod* was received by the Cleveland Coordinating Committee from Cod, Inc., in 1975. Never modified by the navy during the post–World War II period, she has not even been cut open for public access, thus preserving her original condition.

Outdoor displays include a working periscope, armaments, torpedoes, and the submarine.

Admission
Entry fee. Open daily, 10 A.M.–5 P.M., May–Labor Day.

COSHOCTON
Roscoe Village Foundation

Roscoe Village Foundation
440 North Whitewoman Street
Coshocton, OH 43812
(614) 622-9310

Location
About seventy miles northeast of Columbus and ninety-five miles southwest of Cleveland, Coshocton is on State Rtes. 16 and 83 near the junction with Rte. 36.

Highlights
Replica canal barge
Five-building exhibit tour
Horse-drawn trolley ride
1890 bed and breakfast
Country inn (fifty-one rooms)
Gift shops

General Information
Roscoe Village is a restored 1830s Ohio and Erie Canal town in America's heartland. This relatively out-of-the-way section of east-central Ohio was once a total wilderness with no outlet for its produce except by primitive wagon roads or infrequent river rafts/boats. The idea of an inland waterway connecting Lake Erie to the Ohio River was thus revolutionary, and the advent of cheap inland transportation changed Ohio almost overnight.

On display are canal artifacts, models of a lock and a gristmill, a blacksmith shop, a one-room schoolhouse, the residence/office of a canal physician, plus a craft and learning center. A seasonal seventy-eight foot, twenty-five ton replica of an 1830s packet (a passenger boat carrying mail and cargo regularly), drawn by a team of horses, carries passengers along a restored tree-shaded section of the canal.

Roscoe Village is host to fourteen restored, eight preserved, two reconstructed, and four new buildings that house twenty-one shops, five restaurants, and multiple exhibits.

Activities
Canal boat rides (seasonal), horse-drawn trolley rides (seasonal), five-building exhibit tour, Johnson-Humrickhouse Museum, shopping, walking, jogging, and bicycling on the towpath

Admission
Entry fee for Canal boat ride, trolley ride, and five-building exhibit tour. Open daily, 1 P.M.–5 P.M., Memorial Day–October.

Johnson-Humrickhouse Museum: no entry fee. Open daily, noon–5 P.M., May–October; Tuesday–Sunday, 1 P.M.–4:30 P.M., November–April.

FAIRPORT HARBOR
Fairport Marine Museum

Fairport Marine Museum
129 Second Street
Fairport Harbor, OH 44077
(216) 354-4825

Location
Fairport Harbor is twenty-three miles northeast of Cleveland on Lake Erie. Take I-90 east to SR-44, then north into Fairport Harbor.

Highlights
Pilothouse from the SS *Frontenac*
Fairport lighthouse tower

General Information
The Fairport Marine Museum, founded in 1945, is housed in the 1871 Fairport lighthouse and keeper's residence. Exhibits include: collections of navigation instruments; marine charts; manuscripts; pictures and paintings of ships; lanterns; lighthouse lenses; ship carpenter's tools; models and half-hulls of ships; iron ore; Indian relics; and the pilothouse from the laker *Frontenac*.

A midwinter scene along the long wharf at Cincinnati on the Ohio River, with about ten sternwheelers and sidewheelers tied up in the ice, in a photograph taken by E. J. Carpenter on 24 January 1893. (All rights reserved; Rosenfeld Collections, Mystic Seaport Museum, Inc.)

A library of marine books is available for use by appointment, and there is an observation tower for viewing the surrounding area.

Activities
Guided tours

Admission
Entry fee. Memberships are available. Open Saturdays, Sundays, and holidays, 1 P.M.–6 P.M., Memorial Day–Labor Day. By appointment only for groups.

MARIETTA
Ohio River Museum

Campus Maritus/Ohio River
Museum Complex
601 Second Street
Marietta, OH 45750
(614) 373-3750 or 1-800-BUCKEYE

Location
Marietta lies in southeast Ohio on the Ohio River near the West Virginia state line. Take I-77 south from Cambridge.

Highlights
The *W. P. Snyder, Jr.* (1918 stern-wheeler)
Nineteenth-century steamboat artifacts and models
Pilothouse from the *Tell City* (the nation's oldest riverboat)
Gift shop

General Information
The Ohio River Museum was founded in 1941. Its exhibits include: the 1918 stern-wheeler *W. P. Snyder, Jr.,* the last steam-powered towboat of her type; the pilothouse from the steam packet (a passenger boat carrying mail and cargo regularly) *Tell City;* an audiovisual presentation of the ecological, recreational, and commercial history of the Ohio River, from its origin to the present; scale models of nineteenth-century riverboats; and pictures, whistles, and a full-size steam calliope.

Activities
Guided tours of the *W. P. Snyder, Jr.,* a twenty-minute multiscreen slide presentation on Ohio River history, and special school-group programs

Admission
Entry fee. Group discounts. Open Wednesday–Saturday, 9:30 A.M.–5 P.M., Sunday, noon–5 P.M., March, April, October, and November; Monday–Saturday, 9:30 A.M.–5 P.M., Sundays and holidays, noon–5 P.M., May–September. Closed December, Jan-

The *W. P. Snyder, Jr.*, a 1918 stern-wheeler used on the Ohio River to tow barges—sometimes eight or more at a time. She is now a part of the Ohio River Museum at Marietta, Ohio.

uary, and February. (The *W. P. Snyder, Jr.* opens 15 April and closes the last weekend in October. Hours are the same as the museum's.)

VERMILION
Great Lakes Historical Society Museum

Great Lakes Historical Society Museum
480 Main Street
Vermilion, OH 44089-1099
(216) 967-3467

Location
Vermilion is thirty-five miles west of Cleveland on I-80/90.

Highlights
The *William G. Mather* (1926 iron-ore freighter)
Ship models
Inland Seas (quarterly)
The Chadburn (newsletter)
The Metcalf Memorial Library (2,000 volumes)
Museum store

General Information

The Great Lakes Historical Society Museum, founded in 1944, returns visitors to August 1679, when Sieur de La Salle sailed his *Griffon* (the first white man's vessel on the Lakes) west and north in search of furs, only to disappear and become the first legend of the Lakes. Exhibits span a 300-year period, all the way to the loss of the *Edmund Fitzgerald.*

The pictures, paintings, models, and marine artifacts help viewers return to the period of our country's greatest development. By taking the wheel on the simulated ship's bridge, a visitor can become a master for a moment on a giant bulk carrier. The museum store contains a fine selection of history-related stories.

In 1990 the museum will open the *William G. Mather,* an 18-foot, 13,500-ton iron-ore freighter built in 1926. The vessel was donated by the Cleveland Cliffs Iron Company, founded by Mr. Mather. Visitors may tour the pilot deck, crew quarters, galley, engine room, staterooms, and four cargo holds.

The Clarence S. Metcalf Library in the museum contains one of the largest collections of books, periodicals, records, and photographs of Great Lakes vessels, facilities, and maritime activities to be found anywhere.

Activities

Boat shows, fairs, model shipbuilding

Admission

Entry fee. Memberships are available. Open daily, 10 A.M.–5 P.M. in spring, summer, and fall; 10 A.M.–5 P.M. in the winter.

NEW YORK (WESTERN)

BUFFALO

Buffalo and Erie Counties Naval and Servicemen's Park

Naval and Servicemen's Park
One Naval Park Cove
Buffalo, NY 14202
(716) 847-1773

Location
Buffalo lies at the west end of upper New York state on Lake Erie. The park is immediately east of the junction of I-190 and Rte. 5, south of the city's center.

Highlights
The USS *The Sullivans* (DD 537) (destroyer)
The USS *Little Rock* (CLG 4) (guided missile light cruiser)
The USS *Croaker* (submarine)

General Information
The Naval and Servicemen's Park is one of the few inland naval parks in the country. Visitors may board two frontline fighting ships—the guided-missile cruiser USS *Little Rock* and the destroyer USS *The Sullivans*. *The Sullivans* is a lasting memorial to the five Sullivan brothers who gave their lives with the sinking of the USS *Juneau* during World War II.

Snooks 2nd, one of the 9,500 P-39 airacobras built in Buffalo and Niagara Falls, is also on display. After World War II the plane was abandoned in the jungles of New Guinea and was later salvaged and donated to the Park. Additionally, the museum holds model shipbuilder Jim Gillis's ship and object collection.

Activities
Guided tours, audiovisual programs, overnight encampment programs, and social engagements aboard the USS *Little Rock*

Admission
Entry fee. Open daily, 10 A.M.–dusk, 1 June–31 October; Saturdays and Sundays only, 10 A.M.–5 P.M., November.

DUNKIRK
Point Gratiot Lighthouse

Point Gratiot Lighthouse
and Veterans Park Museum
P.O. Box 69
Dunkirk, NY 14048
(716) 366-5050

Location
Dunkirk is both forty miles southwest of Buffalo on I-90 and forty miles northeast of Erie, Pa., off SR-5.

Highlights
Historic lighthouse
Veterans Museum

General Information
Point Gratiot Lighthouse (established in 1875) is near a public park on the west side of the harbor. The light acted in tandem with a pier-head beacon to guide ships to the safety of Dunkirk Harbor.

The Veterans Park Museum consists of seven display rooms, five of which are for each branch of the service: Coast Guard, Marine Corps, Navy, Army, and Air Force. The other two rooms honor the lighthouse keeper and Vietnam War Veterans.

Admission
Entry fee. Open daily, 10 A.M.–3 P.M., April–June; 10 A.M.–4 P.M., July–August; 10 A.M.–2 P.M., September–November.

SACKETS HARBOR
Sackets Harbor Battlefield State Historic Site

Sackets Harbor Battlefield State Historic Site
503 West Main Street (or P.O. Box 27)
Sackets Harbor, NY 13685
(315) 646-3634/3636

Location
From Syracuse take I-81 north to SR-3. Follow it west nine miles to Sackets Harbor on Lake Ontario. The site is located at 505 West Washington Street at the west end of the village.

Highlights
U.S. Navy shipyard
War of 1812 historical information
Battlefield of 29 May 1813 where 800 British, Canadian, and Indian troops from Canada failed in a six-hour battle to destroy this major American shipyard on Lake Ontario

General Information
Sackets Harbor Battlefield State Historic Site, founded in 1933, is a historic American navy yard and battlefield complex that is housed in six buildings: the 1818 Union Hotel; the restored 1849 Commandant's and Master's houses; the 1848 stable; the 1850 icehouse; and the 1840 farmhouse. All of these are located on a nineteenth-century naval base that played an important part in the War of 1812.

Sackets Harbor was settled in 1801 and quickly became a flourishing Lake Ontario port. During the War of 1812 it was the center of U.S. naval and military activity along the upper St. Lawrence River. The unfinished first-rate ship of the line the USS *New Orleans,* designed to carry a crew of 1,000, was enclosed in a huge wooden shiphouse to protect it for future use. In 1883 the navy decided to scrap the vessel. By doing so, together with improved Canadian-American relations, the need for a naval base at Sackets Harbor ended. The navy maintained the facility until the 1960s, and it was seldom used except by the state's naval militia.

Collections include a restored thirteen room 1850–61 navy commandant's house and outbuildings, War of 1812 weapons, armament accessories, military clothing, and nineteenth-century household furniture and accessories.

Activities
Guided and self-guided tours during the summer, military encampments, picnic area, Christmas open house, lectures, special summer programs, and Visitor's Center

Admission
No entry fee. Open Tuesday–Saturday, 10 A.M.–5 P.M., Sunday, 1 P.M.–5 P.M., late May–mid-September. Other times by appointment.

SYRACUSE

Canal Society of New York State

Canal Society of New York State, Inc.
311 Montgomery Street
Syracuse, NY 13202
(315) 428-1862

Location
Take I-690 into Syracuse. Exit onto Erie Street, which intersects with Montgomery.

Highlights
Library (300 volumes)

General Information
Canal Society of New York State, founded in 1956, is a historical museum with a collection of graphics on the history of New York State canals. A library is available for research on the premises.

Activities
Guided tours, lectures, research on New York State canals

Admission
No entry fee. Memberships are available. Open by appointment only.

Erie Canal Museum

Erie Canal Museum
Weighlock Building
Erie Boulevard East and Montgomery Street
Syracuse, NY 13202
(315) 471-0593

Location
Take either east-west I-90 or north-south I-81 into Syracuse. The museum is located near the downtown area in the Weighlock building on the corner of Erie Boulevard East and Montgomery Street.

Highlights
Full-size canal boat
Nation's leading Erie Canal collection
Canal Packet (newsletter)
Gift shop

General Information
The Erie Canal is a symbol of American ingenuity; it captures the spirit of a young nation striving to achieve its dreams. The construction of this inland waterway is a story of determination and innovation, unheard of engineering feats, and, ultimately, the triumph of mankind over nature. The Erie Canal Museum, founded in 1962, is housed in the Weighlock Building, the last administrative structure in use on the Erie Canal. Visitors may explore the beginnings, construction, use, life, and effects of this great symbol.

A thirty-five-mile stretch of the canal is preserved in Old Erie Canal State Park. Starting near Syracuse in Dewitt and extending to New London near Rome, the park provides an excellent hiking and biking trail on the original towpath trod by mules and horses in the 1800s. The Canal Center, operated by the Erie Canal Museum, sits on the edge of the towpath in the Dewitt portion of the state park. The center's exhibits introduce visitors to the types of canal structures seen throughout the park, and it houses the museum's full-size historic canal boat collection.

Activities
Group tours, weekend workshops, and special events. Visitors may board the canal boat to experience canal life and work.

Admission
Entry fee. Open Tuesday–Sunday, 10 A.M.–5 P.M., year-round. Closed Thanksgiving, Christmas, and New Year's Day.

PENNSYLVANIA (WESTERN)

ERIE
Erie Historical Museum and Planetarium

Erie Historical Museum
and Planetarium
356 West Sixth Street
Erie, PA 16507
(814) 453-5811

Location
Erie is on the lakefront along I-90, which runs east/west from New York to Ohio. At the junction with I-79 head north to Erie. The museum is just west of Gannon University Campus on Lake Erie.

Highlights
Planetarium
Ship models
Library (500 volumes)

General Information
The Erie Historical Museum and Planetarium was founded in 1899. It offers exhibits on regional and maritime history, among which are multimedia presentations on the history of commercial fishing in Erie and the battle of Lake Erie during the War of 1812. The exhibits include ship models and historical artifacts, and the battle of Lake Erie exhibit features talking figures of Oliver Hazard Perry and Daniel Dobbins.

A library of letters, documents, and books on local history is available for research. In addition, a research planetarium has shows every Saturday and Sunday at 2 P.M. and 3 P.M.

Activities
Guided tours, lectures, films, and a Victorian Christmas show

Admission
Entry fee. Memberships are available. Open Tuesday–Sunday, 1 P.M.–5 P.M., September–May; Tuesday–Friday, 10 A.M.–5 P.M., Saturdays and Sundays, 1 P.M.–5 P.M., June–August.

ILLINOIS

CHICAGO

Chicago Maritime Society

Chicago Maritime Society
North Pier Building
435 East Illinois Street
Chicago, IL 60611
(312) 836-4343

Location
The society's headquarters are at North Pier (near downtown Chicago), on the lower level of the east end facing Ogden Slip and the Chicago River.

Highlights
1939 Coast Guard rescue boat
Canoe and small-craft collection
Chicago Maritime News (semi-annual newsletter)
Library (250 volumes, miscellaneous periodicals and photographs)
Gift shop

General Information
The Chicago Maritime Society, founded in 1982, contains a U.S. Coast Guard rescue surfboat; a canoe and small-craft collection; a seven-foot scale reproduction of *Ra II,* a forty-foot reed sailing boat; a 1940s old town sailing dinghy; and a photograph and manuscript collection.

The museum is housed in the restored North Pier, a waterfront warehouse built in 1905 on the north bank of Ogden Slip between Lake Shore Drive and McClurg Court. It is now the cornerstone of a fifty-acre development in the Streeterville neighborhood east of Michigan Avenue.

Recently, divers found the 200-foot *Wells Burt,* a well-preserved wreck that sank more than a century ago off of Evanston while on a coal run. The hull appears to be in good shape and may add to knowledge of early Great Lakes shipboard life.

Activities
Lectures, films, and concerts

Admission
No entry fee. Memberships are available. Open Tuesday–Sunday, noon–5 P.M., year-round.

SS *Clipper*

SS *Clipper*
Navy Pier
600 East Grand Avenue
Chicago, IL 60611
(312) 329-1800

Location
The *Clipper* is moored near downtown Chicago on the lakefront at Lake Shore Drive and Randolph Street.

Highlights
The SS *Clipper* (retired 1905 Great Lakes passenger steamer)

General Information
The SS *Clipper,* established in 1980, is a 361-foot Great Lakes passenger steamer, itself a museum. She was rebuilt in 1940, having previously been named the *Juniata* and the *Milwaukee Clipper*. Collections include vessel furniture, artifacts, photographs, documents, and printed material.

Activities
Guided tours (May–September), lectures, and education programs

Admission
Call or write the museum for information about their opening hours.

U-505 (German Submarine)

U-505 (Submarine)
Museum of Science and Industry
57th Street and Lake Shore Drive
Chicago, IL 60637
(312) 684-1414

Location
The submarine is housed in the Chicago Museum of Science and Industry (on the south side of Chicago near the lake front) at 57th Street and South Lake Shore Drive.

Highlights
German U-boat

General Information
The German World War II U-505 is the first enemy man-of-war captured by the U.S. Navy since the War of 1812.

An audio cassette contains interviews with captured Germans and an explanation of their shipboard life.

Activities
Tour of the U-boat, and film of the capture

Admission
No entry fee for the Museum of Science and Industry. Open Monday–Friday, 9:30 A.M.–4 P.M., Saturdays, Sundays and year-round, 9:30 A.M.–5 P.M. Entry fee for the U-505. Open Monday–Friday, 9:30 A.M.–4 P.M., Saturdays, Sundays, and holidays, 9:30 A.M.–5:30 P.M., year-round. Closed Christmas.

LOCKPORT

Illinois and Michigan Canal Museum

Illinois and Michigan Canal Museum
803 South State Street
Lockport, IL 60441
(815) 838-5080

Location

Lockport is seven miles northeast of Joliet on SR-171. The museum is one block north of the junction of SR-7.

Highlights

Canal history

Newsletters

General Information

The Illinois and Michigan Canal Museum, founded in 1969, is housed in the 150-year-old canal commissioner's office and residence building. It is the only canal museum in the United States that illustrates the construction, operation, and demise of a single waterway. The museum is owned and operated by the Will County Historical Society and is part of the National Heritage Corridor-Illinois administered by the National Park Service.

The first stop in the museum is the canal room, where many of the century-old artifacts and pictures and documents relevant to the history of the building and operation of the canal are displayed. The canal opened in 1848, and over ten million tons of commerce traversed the canal during its sixty-two years of operation.

Collections include: artifacts, pictures, and documents relevant to the history of the canal; a log cabin and root cellar; a village jail; blacksmith shop, tinsmith shop, workshop, and railroad station; a one-room country school; a smokehouse and herb garden; a settlement house; and a mid-nineteenth-century farmhouse.

The massive stone walls of the first lock built on the canal remain, but the wood gates are gone. Interpretive signs allow visitors to envision how the lock might have been when it held water to a depth of six feet and "locked" boats through.

Activities

Guided tours

Admission

No entry fee. Memberships are available. Open daily, 1 P.M.–4 P.M., January–mid-December. Closed national holidays and Thanksgiving week.

PEORIA
Belle Reynolds (Riverboat)

Belle Reynolds (Riverboat)
c/o Boatworks
Foot of Main Street
Peoria, IL 61602
(309) 673-2628

Location
Peoria is on east/west I-74 about 120 miles southwest of Chicago on the Illinois River.

Highlights
The *Belle Reynolds* (riverboat)
Illinois River history

General Information
The *Belle Reynolds,* a towboat, travels to several area cities along the Illinois River with an exhibit that features historic photographs and artifacts recounting the Illinois River valley from prehistoric times until now. The focus is on the period from 1890 to 1930, when fishing and musseling were extremely important occupations on the river. She currently carries a display about the history of Peoria.

The *Clinton, Davenport, Rock Island, & Fulton Daily Packet* (c. 1900) of the J. S. Line plied the upper Mississippi River serving the Missouri-Iowa-Illinois region. (Photo: Jerry MacMullen Library, Maritime Museum of San Diego.)

Activities
The traveling gallery stops at Hennepin, Illini State Park at Marseilles, and Joliet to the north; Morris, Starved Rock State Park, Henry, Lacon, Chillocothe, Havana, Beardstown, Alton, and St. Louis to the south. On the way back upstream to Peoria, the exhibit stops at Grafton, Hardin, Meredosia, and Pekin.

Admission
Call or write the sponsor for information about the boat's schedule.

INDIANA

JEFFERSONVILLE
Howard Steamboat Museum

Howard Steamboat Museum, Inc.
Clark County Historical Society
1101 East Market Street
P.O. Box 606
Jeffersonville, IN 47131
(812) 283-3728

Location
Jeffersonville lies on the Ohio River across from Louisville, Kentucky. Take the Court Avenue exit off I-65 to the intersection of Spring Street. Head south to Market, then east to the museum.

Highlights
History of the Howard Shipyards
Boat models

General Information
Clark County Historical Society's Howard Steamboat Museum was founded in 1958 and is located in the 1893 historic home of Edmunds J. Howard, son of Howard Shipyards' founder James E. Howard. The museum itself is famous for its original furnishings, and displays include artifacts and scale models of famous steamboats.

In addition, the museum contains information about the original Howard Shipyards (1834–1941). Howard built his first steamboat, the *Hyperion,* in 1834. Quickly thereafter, Howard sidewheelers became noted for their beauty and durability. When James Howard died in 1876, a new era began—that of the sternwheeler.

The shipyards' letterhead boasted of their being "the oldest continuously operated shipyard in America." During World War II they produced landing ship tanks, marking the end of shipbuilding by the Howard family.

Among the 3,000 steamboats built by the Howard family were: the *Glendy Burke* (1851), the *Robt. E. Lee* (1876), the *J. M. White* (1878), the *City of Louisville* (1894), the *Cape Girardeau* (1924), which was later renamed the *Gordon C. Greene* and appeared in the film classic "Gone with the Wind."

Activities
Guided tours, lectures, and work/study for students

Admission
Entry fee. Memberships are available. Open Tuesday–Saturday, 10 A.M.–3 P.M., Sunday, 1 P.M.–3 P.M., year-round. Closed national holidays.

METAMORA
Whitewater Canal State Historic Site

Whitewater Canal State
Historic Site
Box 88
Metamora, IN 47030
(317) 647-6512

Location
Metamora is sixty-one miles southeast of Indianapolis on Rte. 52.

Highlights
Six-mile restored canal section

General Information
Whitewater Canal State Historic Site is adjacent to a fourteen-mile section (six miles of which is restored) of the old waterway built between 1836 and 1845. The restored gristmill produces cornmeal, corn grits, cereal, and whole-wheat flour which can be purchased. And where else can one take a thirty-minute cruise in a horse-drawn canal boat? The ride from Metamora through the Whitewater Valley, across the only covered aqueduct in existence, to Lock 24 at Millville, and back is charming.

Activities
Concerts are periodically staged in a nineteenth-century-style gazebo, and picnicking facilities are near the gristmill.

Admission
Gristmill: no entry fee. Open Tuesday–Friday, 9 A.M.–5 P.M., Saturday, 10 A.M.–6 P.M., and Sunday, 11 A.M.–6 P.M., year-round. Closed national holidays.

Canal boat: entry fee. Open Tuesday–Friday, noon–3:30 P.M., Saturday, 10:30 A.M.–5:45 P.M., and Sunday, 11:30 A.M.–5:45 P.M., June–October.

MICHIGAN CITY
Old Lighthouse Museum

Old Lighthouse Museum
P.O. Box 512
Michigan City, IN 46360
(219) 872-6133/3273

Location
Michigan City at the southern end of Lake Michigan, twenty-five miles east of Gary via I-94. The museum is on Heisman Harbor Road in Washington Park at the city's harbor.

Highlights
Lighthouse
Old Lighthouse Museum News (newsletter)
Library (300 volumes)

General Information
Old Lighthouse Museum was founded in 1973 and is housed in an 1858 lighthouse, Indiana's only one. It was here, in 1847, that the first submarine to ply the Great Lakes (built by L. D. Phillips) was launched.

The museum portrays the long and interesting history of Michigan City, bound to the lake with all its mysteries and beauties. Featured are a keeper's living room and bedroom, a Fresnel lens, stories of shipwrecks, shipbuilding tools, and the top of Abraham Lincoln's funeral train. Collections include lighthouse artifacts, boatbuilder's tools, shipwreck artifacts, local Indian artifacts, and early farm tools.

A library of materials on county and area history and shipping is available for use by appointment.

Activities
Guided tours, lectures, and library

Admission
Entry fee. Memberships are available. Open Tuesday–Sunday, 1 P.M.–4 P.M., year-round. Other times by appointment. Closed Thanksgiving, Christmas, New Year's Day, Good Friday, Easter, Memorial Day, and July Fourth.

IOWA

DUBUQUE
Fred W. Woodward Riverboat Museum

Fred W. Woodward Riverboat Museum
2nd Street Harbor
P.O. Box 305
Dubuque, IA 52001
(319) 557-9545

Location
Dubuque is on the Mississippi River sixty-four miles north of Davenport via I-80.

Highlights
The *William M. Black* (1934 riverboat)
National Rivers Hall of Fame
Newsletter
"The River Adventure" (film)
Harbor shop

General Information
Fred W. Woodward Riverboat Museum was founded in 1979 and exhibits artifacts of upper Mississippi River canoes, towboats, flatboats, steamboats, and steam engines.

Of special note are the *William M. Black,* a former U.S. Army Corps of Engineers sidewheel dredge, and the National Rivers Hall of Fame, established to honor men and women of the inland waters, to collect and preserve river artifacts, and to conduct seminars and educational programs.

Activities
Guided tours, school programs, and publications

Admission
Entry fee. Memberships are available. Open daily, 10 A.M.–6:30 P.M., May–October; Tuesday–Sunday, 10 A.M.–4 P.M., November–December. Closed national holidays.

KEOKUK
Keokuk River Museum

Keokuk River Museum
Johnson and Victory Park
P.O. Box 268
Keokuk, IA 52632
(319) 524-4765

Location
Keokuk lies on the Mississippi River in the southeast tip of Iowa, right at the Missouri state line. Take I-380 directly south out of Cedar Rapids.

Highlights
The *George M. Verity* (paddlewheel steamboat)

General Information
Keokuk River Museum, founded in 1961, is housed in the *George M. Verity,* a Mississippi River steamboat. Originally the SS *Thorpe* when she was built by the U.S. government in 1927 at Dubuque, the *Verity* (renamed for the founder of the Armco Steel Corporation) inaugurated barge service on the upper Mississippi. The first of four steamboats built to revive river transportation, she was also the first to move barges from St. Louis north to St. Paul. The *Verity* was retired in 1960 after thirty-three years of service on the Mississippi and Ohio Rivers. Now berthed at Johnson and Victory Park, she houses a museum of upper Mississippi River history and beckons visitors to come aboard.

Activities
Lectures

Admission
Entry fee. Open daily, 9 A.M.–5 P.M., mid-April–November.

LE CLAIRE

Buffalo Bill Museum of Le Claire

Buffalo Bill Museum of
Le Claire, Iowa, Inc.
Foot of Jones Street
Le Claire, IA 52753
(319) 289-5580

Location
Le Claire is on the Mississippi River ten miles north of the tri-cities area (Davenport, Rock Island, and Moline). Immediately off I-80, follow River Drive to the foot of Jones Street on the levee.

Highlights
The *Lone Star Steamer* (stern-wheeler)
Gift shop

General Information
Buffalo Bill Museum of Le Claire, founded in 1957, was created to preserve the history of Le Claire through its river captains, pilots, shipyards, and other areas of maritime interest. Exhibits include the *Lone Star Steamer,* one of the last working riverboats on the Mississippi River, which was decommissioned in 1966 and drydocked in 1968. Also on display is the work of James Ryan, inventor of the flight recorder for airplanes and seat belts.

Admission
Entry fee. Open daily, 7:30 A.M.–4:30 P.M. in summer; Saturdays and Sundays, 7:30 A.M.–4:30 P.M. in winter.

SEVEN

CENTRAL

MANITOBA, CANADA

SELKIRK
Marine Museum of Manitoba

Marine Museum of Manitoba
Box 7
Selkirk, Manitoba R1A 2B1
Canada
(204) 482-7761

Location
The museum is in Selkirk Park at the corner of Eveline and Queen Streets. Selkirk is on the Red River, twenty minutes northeast of Winnipeg on PTH-9.

Highlights
The SS *Keenora* (lake steamer)
The CGS *Bradbury* (steam vessel c. 1915)
The MS *Peguis II* (tugboat)
The MS *Lady Canadian* (fish freighter)
The *Chickama II* (passenger vessel)

General Information
Manitoba's history comes to life in the Marine Museum of Manitoba, founded in 1972. The museum reflects Selkirk's nautical past through displays of outboard motors, tools used in shipbuilding in the early 1900s, and three restored ships. The SS *Keenora,* a steamer built in 1897, was brought to Lake Winnipeg in 1923 and houses nautical artifacts and photographs. The CGS *Bradbury,* a steam vessel built in 1915, and the CGS *Peguis II,* a tugboat, house documents of the marine history of the Red River and Lake Winnipeg. A lighthouse from Lake Winnipeg is also on display.

Vessels recently acquired are the MS *Lady Canadian* (1942), a former fish freighter, and the *Chickama II* (1944), a former riverboat used for passengers and freight. Because of its shallow draft, it took passengers from Warren's Landing to Norway House, where deep-draft vessels could not go.

Admission
Entry fee. Open Monday–Saturday, 9 A.M.–6 P.M., Sundays and holidays, 10 A.M.–6 P.M., May–June; daily and holidays, 10 A.M.–6 P.M., July–August.

SOUTH DAKOTA

SIOUX FALLS
Battleship *South Dakota* Museum

Battleship *South Dakota* Museum
805 South Kiwanis
Sioux Falls, SD 57104
(605) 339-7059

Location
Sioux Falls is at the junction of I-29 north/south and I-90 east/west. The museum is on 12th Street (just east of I-29) at the corner of South Kiwanis.

Highlights
The USS *South Dakota* (battleship model)

General Information
The Battleship *South Dakota* Museum, founded in 1968, is a military and nautical museum that exhibits memorabilia from the battleship USS *South Dakota,* silver services, gun barrels, a scale model of the ship, books, photographs, anchors, and flags.

Activities
Films and crew member reunions

Admission
No entry fee. Open daily, 9 A.M.–5 P.M., Memorial Day–Labor Day.

NEBRASKA

BROWNVILLE
Museum of Missouri River History

Museum of Missouri River History
Brownville, NE 68321
(402) 825-3341

Location
Brownville is sixty miles south of Omaha on the Missouri River. Take I-29 south to the Rte. 136 exit, then head west into Brownville.

Highlights
The *Captain Meriwether Lewis* (steamboat dredge)

General Information
Founded in 1986, the Museum of Missouri River History is housed aboard the *Captain Meriwether Lewis,* a historic steam-powered, side-wheel steamboat dredge. This barge spent her entire working life (1932–1969) on the wild, unpredictable, and often dangerous

Missouri River. The museum is now designated as a national historic site. Displayed are artifacts from the Nebraska State Historical Society which show the development of the Missouri River valley from the days when glaciers covered the Midwest to the present time.

Visitors will see what role the massive dredge boat played in taming the mighty Missouri. Giant steam engines and boiler, the wooden paddle wheels, the dining halls, officers' sleeping quarters, and the popular pilothouse, with its bird's-eye view of the river, along with its impressive brass fixtures, are waiting to be seen on board the 268-foot *Lewis*.

Activities
Guided tours

Admission
Entry fee. Open daily, 10 A.M.–5:30 P.M., Memorial Day–Labor Day. Open Saturdays and Sundays only, 10 A.M.–5:30 P.M., May, September, and October.

OKLAHOMA

MUSKOGEE
Muskogee War Memorial Park and Military Museum

Muskogee War Memorial Park
and Military Museum
P.O. Box 253
Muskogee, OK 74401
(918) 682-6294

Location
Muskogee is forty miles southeast of Tulsa on the Arkansas River via SR-51 (a turnpike).

Highlights
The USS *Batfish* (SS-310) (submarine)
Fifty-two lost-boat memorials

General Information
Muskogee War Memorial Park and Military Museum, founded in 1972, exhibits artifacts from all branches of the service—Army, Navy, Marine, and Air Force—particularly the USS *Batfish*. She was commissioned on 5 May 1943 at Portsmouth, New Hampshire, and entered World War II in 1944. Almost thirty years later, she was berthed in Muskogee, where she is fully open to the public. Visitors may tour the maneuvering room, the diving station, the control room, and the after-torpedo tubes.

Activities
Guided tours

Admission
Entry fee. Open Monday–Saturday, 9 A.M.–5 P.M., Sunday, noon–5 P.M., 15 March–15 October.

EIGHT

PACIFIC NORTHWEST

BRITISH COLUMBIA, CANADA

NEW WESTMINISTER
Samson V Maritime Museum

Samson V Maritime Museum
75 Mott Crescent
New Westminister, British Columbia V3L 4L8
Canada
(604) 521-7656

Location
New Westminister lies on Rte. 91 immediately south of Vancouver. The museum is on the waterfront between 8th and 10th Streets.

Highlights
The *Samson V* (stern-wheeler)
Maritime history

General Information
Founded in 1983, the *Samson V* Maritime Museum is aboard the stern-wheeler of the same name, the last to operate on the Fraser River. Collections include vessel preservation, maritime collections, and photographs.

Activities
Tours arranged by appointment, and special programs

Admission
No entry fee, but donations accepted. Open Saturdays, Sundays, and holidays, noon–5 P.M., year-round.

TOFINO
West Coast Maritime Museum

West Coast Maritime Museum
4111 Campbell Street/P.O. Box 421
Tofino, British Columbia V0R 2Z0
Canada
(604) 725-3163

Location
From Victoria, Vancouver Island, take Rte. 1 north about 86 miles to the junction with Rte. 4. Head west about 120 miles to Tofino (on Clayoquet Sound) on the west coast of Vancouver Island.

Highlights
Whale Center
Displays
Cruise

General Information
The West Coast Maritime Museum, founded in 1969, features maritime and fishing trade history. Bells, equipment, and artifacts from sunken ships, Nootka Indian artifacts, and some species of sea life are displayed.

Activities
Cruise

Admission
No entry fee. Open daily, 11 A.M.–6 P.M., March–June; 10 A.M.–8 P.M., July–October.

VANCOUVER
St. Roch National Historic Site

St. Roch National Historic Site
Canadian Parks Service
1905 Ogden Avenue
Vancouver, British Columbia V6J 1A3
Canada
(604) 666-3201

Location
In Vancouver head west on Marine Drive to Ogden Street. The site is at the foot of Cypress Street, Vanier Park, at the Vancouver Maritime Museum.

Highlights
The *St. Roch* (pronounced ROCK) (1928 Royal Canadian Mounted Police Arctic patrol boat)

General Information
St. Roch National Historic Site was founded in 1974 and exhibits the *St. Roch,* a Royal Canadian Mounted Police Arctic patrol vessel displayed as it appeared in 1944. Housed in a contemporary A-frame building, it is adjacent to and a part of the Vancouver Maritime Museum.

During World War II she became the first vessel to travel from the Pacific to the Atlantic via the treacherous Northwest Passage in the Arctic. In 1944 the *St. Roch* returned from Halifax, Nova Scotia, to Vancouver, British Columbia, marking the first successful round-trip voyage through the Northwest Passage. Assigned to Halifax after the war, the schooner reached its destination by going through the Panama Canal, thus becoming the first vessel to circumnavigate the North American continent.

Activities
St. Roch movie, and guided tours in French and English; group bookings encouraged.

Admission
Entry fee. Open daily, 10 A.M.–6 P.M., year-round.

Vancouver Maritime Museum

Vancouver Maritime Museum
1905 Ogden Avenue
Vancouver, British Columbia V6J 1A3
Canada
(604) 737-2211

Location
In Vancouver go west on Marine Drive to 1905 Ogden Avenue, at the foot of Cypress Street. The museum adjoins the Vancouver Museum/H.R. Macmillan Planetarium/Gordon Southham Observatory complex.

Highlights
The *St. Roch* (Royal Canadian Mounted Police Arctic patrol vessel)
International heritage vessels at adjoining Heritage Harbour
Ship models

General Information
British Columbia's rich maritime heritage is housed at the Vancouver Maritime Museum on the shores of Kitsilano's Hadden Park. Built in 1959, the museum is the only institution on the mainland to document the cultural and material history of the generations of British Columbians who have drawn their livelihood from the sea. Its particular focus is on the Port of Vancouver—from the first explorers to enter its waters to today's international cruise ship facility.

Adjoining the Museum is the *St. Roch* (pronounced ROCK), the Royal Canadian Mounted Police's Arctic patrol vessel that was the first ship to sail the Northwest Passage from the Pacific to the Atlantic Ocean.

A unique feature of the Vancouver Maritime Museum is Heritage Harbour, with its revolving display vessels ranging from locally built yachts to restored schooners and replicas of historic ships. Following EXPO '86, the Heritage Harbour collection was expanded to include international heritage vessels such as a Chinese junk (a flat-bottomed ship with battened sails), a Venetian gondola, and the *Antar Bangsa,* a gaff-rigged cargo vessel from Indonesia.

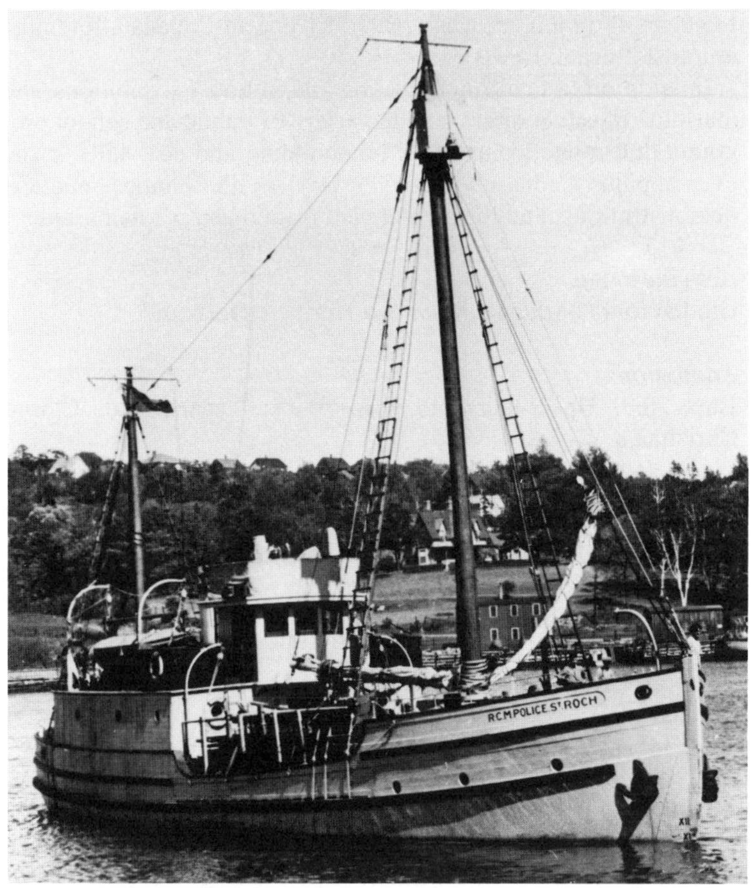

The *St. Roch* is a fully restored two-masted ketch built in 1928 for the Royal Canadian Mounted Police as an Arctic patrol vessel. She sailed the Northwest Passage in both directions, completely circumnavigating the continent of North America. In 1962 the *St. Roch* was designated a national historic site and is now permanently housed in a covered drydock adjacent to the Vancouver Maritime Museum in Vancouver, British Columbia, Canada.

In July 1987 the museum received another important addition—a sixty-foot-long mural recounting Vancouver's maritime history, unveiled on the west exterior wall of the building. The mural, donated by the legal firm Rand and Edgar under the Vancouver

Legacies Programme, was created by one of Canada's foremost muralists, Frank Lewis.

In addition to featuring traveling and in-house exhibitions, the maritime museum offers a wide variety of public and school programs that range from model boatbuilding and sea skills to the ever-popular Captain Vancouver Day—with shanties, nautical demonstrations, and the annual visit from the city's namesake.

Activities
Guided tours of the *St. Roch* and Heritage Harbour

Admission
Entry fee. Open daily, 10 A.M.–5 P.M., year-round. Closed Christmas.

VICTORIA
Maritime Museum of British Columbia

Maritime Museum of British Columbia
28–30 Bastion Square
Victoria, British Columbia V8W 1H9
Canada
(604) 385-4222

Location
The museum is on Bastion Square (View and Wharf Streets), several blocks north of the Parliament buildings along Victoria's harbor front.

Highlights
The *Tilikum* (dugout)
Ship models
Figureheads
Naval uniforms
Library
Gift shop

General Information

The Maritime Museum of British Columbia, founded in 1955, exhibits a collection of artifacts, documents, models, and pictures on the maritime history of British Columbia, the West Coast of North America, and the Pacific Rim. Located in the historic Provincial Court House (a national heritage building constructed in 1889), the museum depicts British Columbia's maritime tradition, from the days of Captain Cook's early exploration and coastal shipping to the days of the Canadian Pacific Railway ships and the U.S. Navy in the Pacific Northwest.

The famous *Tilikum,* sailed by Captain Voss from Victoria to England (1901–04), is housed in the museum. Also displayed is the *Trekka,* built in Victoria by John Guzzwell and sailed by him around the world single-handedly in 1955.

An extensive library of books, photographs, and periodicals is available for society members.

Activities

Films, lectures, and tours for members and the public

Admission

Entry fee. Memberships are available. Open daily, 10 A.M.–6 P.M., July–Labor Day; Monday–Saturday, 10 A.M.–4 P.M., Sunday, noon–4 P.M., the rest of the year. Closed Christmas and New Year's Day.

YUKON TERRITORY

DAWSON CITY
SS *Keno* (Stern-wheeler)

The SS *Keno*
The Klondike National Historic Sites
P.O. Box 390
Dawson, Yukon Y0B 1G0
Canada
(403) 993-5462

Location
From Anchorage, Alaska, travel 243 miles on Rte. 1 to Tok. Then head northeast on Rte. 5/9 the 106 miles to Dawson. The *Keno* is in drydock on Front Street between King and Queen Streets.

Highlights
The SS *Keno* (stern-wheeler)

General Information
The SS *Keno,* relocated to Dawson in 1961, now sits on the bank of the Yukon River. Built in 1922 at Whitehorse, it was the last riverboat to run between that city and Dawson.

Because the stern-wheeler used wood-fired boilers, wood camps were established along the waterway, resulting in an important new industry. The SS *Keno* was part of the fleet that played a major part in the history of the Yukon Territory, bringing out the ore each spring and doing so until the railroad was built, thus eliminating the need for river transportation.

The museum has photo exhibits depicting the *Keno*'s career. An outdoor exhibit shows the life that she played in the Yukon. Today, the SS *Keno* is undergoing restoration.

Activities
Guided tours

Admission
No entry fee. Call or write the sponsors for information about opening hours.

WASHINGTON

ABERDEEN
Grays Harbor Historical Seaport

Grays Harbor Historical Seaport
P.O. Box 2019
Aberdeen, WA 98520-0330
(206) 532-8611

Location
Aberdeen is almost directly west of Olympia on Grays Harbor, off Rte. 101.

Highlights
The *Columbia* (373-ton square-rigged ship)
The *Lady Washington* (170-ton brig)
Active tall ship construction

General Information
The Grays Harbor Historical Seaport Authority was founded in 1987 to construct a seaport, build tall ships, and develop a nautical museum.

The seaport finished building the seventy-two-foot brig *Lady Washington* in the spring of 1989 to commemorate the centennial of Washington's statehood. Lady Washington (the original was named for Martha Washington even before she became first lady), is equipped to carry passengers and is the first replica of a U.S. tall ship ever built.

The other tall ship under construction, the *Columbia,* is scheduled for launching in 1992, 200 years after the original *Columbia* was sailed by Captain Robert Gray in his explorations during which both Grays Harbor and the Columbia River were discovered. (Gray was also the first U.S. sea captain to sail around the world.) The *Columbia* will be certified as a sail-training vessel.

Nautical exhibits, a museum, and other training programs are planned for the seaport.

Admission
Entry fee. Open Monday–Saturday, 10 A.M.–5:30 P.M., Sundays, noon–5 P.M., year-round. Closed Thanksgiving, Christmas, and New Year's Day.

BREMERTON
Bremerton Naval Museum

Bremerton Naval Museum
130 Washington Street
Bremerton, WA 98310
(206) 479-7447

Location
Bremerton is directly west across Puget Sound from Seattle. The museum is on Washington Street, one block from the ferry terminal.

Highlights
"Story of Attack" (a display by the Pearl Harbor Survivors Association)
"Artifacts of the USS *Washington*" (display by CV6 [Enterprise] Association)
Mock-up of a ship's bridge (a hands-on area)
Gift shop

General Information
Bremerton Naval Museum is in a recently refurbished building. Maritime history displays include ship models, early steam engines, naval weapons, naval history, and articles and photos pertaining to the history of the Puget Sound Naval Shipyard.

Admission
No entry fee, but donations accepted. Open Tuesday–Saturday, 10 A.M.–5 P.M., Sunday, 1 P.M.–5 P.M., year-round.

EDMONDS
Edmonds Historical Museum

Edmonds Historical Museum
118 Fifth Avenue North
P.O. Box 52
Edmonds, WA 98020
(206) 774-0900

Location
Edmonds is just eighteen miles north of Seattle on I-5. Exit west on SR-104 into Edmonds to 5th Avenue North in the downtown area.

Highlights
Ship models
Maritime library (150 volumes)
Gift shop

General Information
Edmonds Historical Museum, formally opened in 1973, was established by the Edmonds-South Snohomish County Historical Society to: perpetuate the memory and spirit of the state's pioneers; identify and preserve historical documents, relics, and incidents; and encourage historical research, today and tomorrow.

The ground floor of the museum houses the marine room and an extensive display of photographs of venerable steam passenger vessels and modern auto ferries that depict Edmonds' link with the sea.

Displayed, too, are numerous ship models, marine paintings, navigating instruments, and other marine artifacts. A large diorama of Edmonds' waterfront circa 1910, with a working model of a shingle mill, is an important attraction. There is also a permanent display of the history of the U.S. Coast and Geodetic Survey and its successor, the National Oceanic and Atmospheric Administration which have played an important role in charting this area, following the explorations of Captain George Vancouver in 1792 and Lieutenant Charles Wilkes in 1841.

Admission
No entry fee. Open Tuesday, Thursday, Saturday, and Sunday, 1 P.M.–4 P.M., year-round.

FRIDAY HARBOR–SAN JUAN ISLAND
Whale Museum

Whale Museum
62 First Street North
P.O. Box 945
Friday Harbor, WA 98250
(206) 378-4710

Location
Follow I-5 sixty-six miles north from Seattle to Burlington. Exit onto SR-20, heading west fifteen miles to Anacortes, where ferries leave for San Juan Island and Friday Harbor.

Highlights
Whale models
Library

General Information
The Whale Museum, founded in 1978, occupies one of the island's oldest buildings. Museum exhibits depict the biology, behavior, and sounds of marine mammals. Included are a comparative skeletal display of a human, an otter, and a dolphin, and skeletons of a baby gray whale and an adult orca (killer) whale. Also included are exhibits of baleen and related ethnological artifacts, plus killer, humpback, and sperm whale models.

A library of books and scientific reprints on natural history, ecology, communications, physiology, bioacoustics, general biology of marine mammals, and museology are available for research by request.

Activities
Guided tours, lectures, films, gallery talks, workshops, and a whale school

Admission
Entry fee. Memberships are available. Open daily, 11 A.M.–4 P.M., October–June; 10 A.M.–5 P.M., July–September. Closed Thanksgiving, Christmas, and New Year's Day.

KEYPORT

Naval Undersea Museum

Naval Undersea Museum
Code 016
Keyport, WA 98345
(206) 396-2894/6218

Location
From Bremerton travel twenty miles north on SR-16 to SR-308. Take exits for the Naval Undersea Warfare Engineering Station at Keyport.

Highlights
The *Trieste II* (deep submergence vehicle)
50,000-square-foot museum facility
Japanese Kiaten manned torpedo
Museum store

General Information
The Naval Undersea Museum, founded in 1979, is dedicated to various aspects of undersea history and technology. Dynamic and interactive exhibits promote an understanding of undersea life and naval undersea operations in an entertaining and educational manner. Awaiting completion of a permanent facility, a temporary

museum exhibit is available for viewing. Interested parties should make an appointment at least two days prior to the desired date of visit by calling the number listed above.

Admission
No entry fee. Call or write the museum for information about their opening hours.

SEATTLE
The Center for Wooden Boats

The Center for Wooden Boats
1010 Valley Street
Seattle, WA 98109
(206) 382-2628

Location
The center is on the north side of downtown Seattle at the south end of Lake Union on Valley Street (adjacent to the Northwest Seaport).

Highlights
Traditional boatbuilding
Shavings (newsletter)
Traditional wooden boats for rent

General Information
The Center for Wooden Boats, founded in 1978, is a small watercraft museum and maritime skills preservation center, Seattle's newest waterfront park. The center offers a unique chance to put one's hands to the oars of a rowboat or the tiller of a traditional wooden catboat (a sailboat having a single mast far forward and usually a centerboard). A living museum, its traditional wooden boats are all unique. A new waterfront park is being created with a turn-back-the-clock pavilion on Lake Union.

Activities
Rowboats, sailboats, classes in wooden boat lapstrake (having the exterior planks overlap like the clapboards on a house) construction, and skills preservation

Admission
No entry fee. Memberships are available. Open Monday–Friday, noon–7 P.M., Saturdays, Sundays, and holidays, 10 A.M.–8 P.M., year-round.

Coast Guard Museum/Northwest

Coast Guard Museum/Northwest
Pier 36
1519 Alaskan Way South
Seattle, WA 98134
(206) 286-9608

Location
The museum is located next to the U.S. Coast Guard Station on Pier 36 at Seattle's waterfront near the downtown area.

Highlights
Ship models
Lighthouse and buoy lenses
Photographs (10,000)

General Information
The Coast Guard Museum/Northwest, founded in 1976, exhibits ship models, lighthouse and buoy lenses, uniforms, and a number of nautical artifacts.

Note: Located next to the museum is the Puget Sound Vessel Traffic Center, 4th floor of the main building, which is open to visitors daily, 8 A.M.–4 P.M.

Activities
Pier 36 is the home port for the 400-foot *Polar*-class icebreakers and two of the 378-foot high endurance cutters. They are usually open to visitors Saturdays and Sundays, 1 P.M.–4:30 P.M.

Admission
No entry fee. Memberships are available. Open Monday, Wednesday, and Friday, 10 A.M.–4 P.M., Saturday and Sunday, 1 P.M.–5 P.M., year-round.

Northwest Seaport

Northwest Seaport
1002 Valley
Seattle, WA 98109
(206) 447-9800

Location
The seaport is on the south end of Lake Union on Valley Street (adjacent to the Center for Wooden Boats).

Highlights
Four historic boardable vessels

General Information
Northwest Seaport was founded in 1964 and owns four northwest vessels:

1) The tugboat *Arthur Foss,* built in 1889 in Portland, Oregon, as the *Wallowa* for the Oregon Railway and Navigation Company. Originally equipped with a steam engine, she towed sailing ships across the Columbia Bar.
2) The lightship *Relief #83* was built in Camden, New Jersey, in 1904 for the lighthouse service. She sailed around the Horn to her first station at Blunts Reef, California, thus beginning fifty-six years of lightship duty. She joined the Northwest Seaport's fleet in 1970.
3) The *San Mateo* was built in California in 1922. The 235-foot steam ferry worked San Francisco Bay even after construction was completed on the Golden Gate and Oakland Bay bridges. She joined the Northwest Seaport's fleet in 1979.
4) The *Wawona,* built in 1897 and launched at the yard of Dan Ditlev Bendixsen at Fairhaven, California, was the largest three-masted sailing schooner built in North America. Today, she is the only survivor of the once-immense commercial sailing fleet in the Pacific Northwest. Carrying lumber between West Coast ports for Dolbeer and Carson Company, the *Wawona,* like other coastal schooners, had a reputation for speedy runs down the coast with cargo and a quick return sailing without ballast.

Admission
Entry fee. The *Arthur Foss, Relief #83,* and *San Mateo* are open daily, 10 A.M.–4 P.M., June–August.

OREGON

ASTORIA
Columbia River Maritime Museum

Columbia River Maritime Museum
1792 Marine Drive
Astoria, OR 97103
(503) 325-2323

Location
Astoria is at the mouth of the Columbia River on Rte. 30.

Highlights
The *Columbia* (lightship moored alongside the museum)
Operable submarine periscopes
Ship models
Library
Museum store

General Information
Columbia River Maritime Museum, founded in 1962, is housed in a 37,000-square-foot building that accommodates several salmon fishing boats, a U.S. Coast Guard lifesaving craft, marine engines, operating lighthouse lenses, nautical artifacts, and marine art of all

sorts, as well as a research library and museum store. One can study coastal exploration of the Northwest, the maritime fur trade, navigation, marine safety, shipwrecks of the Northwest coast, fishing, whaling, inland steamboating in the Northwest, shipbuilding on the Columbia River, sailing vessels, steamships, and U.S. naval history.

The museum's largest exhibit is the former U.S. Coast Guard lightship *Columbia* (WLV-604), which served for twenty-eight years. She is the last lightship to see active duty on the Pacific coast off the mouth of the Columbia River.

Activities

The library is accessible by appointment only. Submarine periscope viewing, standing at the wheel of a Columbia River steamboat pilothouse, "taking the conn" on the actual bridge of the World War II destroyer *Knapp*.

Admission

Entry fee. Open daily, 9:30 A.M.–5 P.M., 1 April–30 September; Tuesday–Sunday, 9:30 A.M.–5 P.M., the rest of the year. Closed Thanksgiving and Christmas.

BANDON

Coquille River Lighthouse

Coquille River Lighthouse
Bullards Beach State Park
P.O. Box 25
Bandon, OR 97411
(503) 347-2209

Location

On the southern Oregon shoreline, Bandon is seventeen miles south of Coos Bay at Bullards Beach State Park on Rte. 101. The lighthouse is reached via the road through the picnic area.

Highlights

Lighthouse

General Information
Coquille River Lighthouse, once known as the guardian of "navigator's nightmare" (where river and ocean meet), is at the southern end of the spit. An interpretive exhibit may be viewed during daylight hours in the summer.

In 1963 the Oregon State Parks leased the Coquille River Lighthouse. It was built in 1896 and restored in 1978 by the U.S. Army Corps of Engineers and the Oregon State Parks. In July 1979 six interpretive signs were installed. The lighthouse is no longer in operation but is open for viewing.

Admission
No entry fee. Open daily, 8 A.M.–8 P.M., 15 May–15 September; Saturdays and Sundays only, 8 A.M.–3 P.M., 16 September–14 May.

CASCADE LOCKS
Cascade Locks and Marine Park

Cascade Locks and Marine Park
Marine Park
Cascade Locks, OR 97014
(503) 374-8619/8427

Location
Cascade Locks is on the Columbia River twenty miles east of Portland off I-84/Rte. 30.

Highlights
River locks

General Information
Cascade Locks and Marine Park is a scenic 200-acre riverfront park that contains historic locks, a marina, a museum, and a Visitor's Center. The museum has tools, photographs, and other regional artifacts.

Admission
Open daily, noon–5 P.M., 1 June–1 September. Other times by appointment.

PORTLAND
Oregon Historical Society Museum

Oregon Historical Society Museum
1230 S.W. Park Avenue
Portland, OR 97205
(503) 222-1741

Location
The museum is at the Oregon Historical Center complex in downtown Portland at Southwest Jefferson and Park avenues (just north of Rte. 26 and east of I-405).

Highlights
Ship models
Watercraft models
Publications
Research library
Gift shop

General Information
Founded in 1873, the Oregon Historical Society Museum succeeded the Oregon Pioneer Association and has promoted the preservation and study of Oregon's heritage. The center notes: "steamboats plied wide calm rivers, transporting goods and settlers into the heart of the Northwest. Images of ships, sailing across the sea, . . . or stern-wheelers steaming up the Columbia come readily to mind. Jolly boats, cutters, and launches carried the first Europeans from their ships into the Oregon bays and inland waters."

Besides a variety of permanent and changing exhibits, the center includes a comprehensive regional research library.

Activities
Group tours, special programs, and demonstrations of pioneer crafts at the annual "Wintering-In" harvest festival on Sauvie Island

Admission
No entry fee. Open Monday–Saturday, 10 A.M.–4:45 P.M., year-round.

SOUTHBEACH
Lighthouse—Yaquina Bay

Friends of the Lighthouse
Southbeach State Park
P.O. Box 1350
Southbeach, OR 97365
(503) 265-7509

Location
Southbeach is just one mile south of Newport. The lighthouse is located in the state park on the oceanfront.

Highlights
Fishing history
Yaquina Bay Lighthouse

General Information
Founded in 1948, a small maritime museum is situated in a log cabin near the Yaquina Bay lighthouse. The museum locale is the base for a very large fishing fleet, some of whom fish for other countries as well as the United States.

Newport's lighthouse was built in 1871. It has been renovated and is open under state auspices. Three miles north, the Yaquina Head Lighthouse was built in 1875 to show a more visible light than was possible with the first one. From the exterior observation deck one can observe migrating whales in season.

Admission
No entry fee, but donations accepted. Open Tuesday–Sunday, 10 A.M.–5 P.M., June–September; 11 A.M.–4 P.M., October–May.

NINE

WEST COAST AND HAWAII

CALIFORNIA

CRESCENT CITY
Battery Point Lighthouse

Battery Point Lighthouse
Del Norte County Historical Society
577 H Street
P.O. Box 396
Crescent City, CA 95531
(707) 464-3089

Location
Crescent City is on the Pacific coastline about eighteen miles south of the Oregon state line on Rte. 101. Battery Point Lighthouse is reached by taking Front Street west to the intersection of A Street. Turn south on A one block to the parking area. The lighthouse is 200–300 yards from the mainland and can be reached when the tide is out by walking a trail (used since 1856) this short distance.

Highlights
Lighthouse
Research files, newspapers, etc.

General Information
Battery Point Lighthouse was built in 1856 and now contains collections in machine, naval, regional, and shipping history. Included are local history books, photographs, diaries, manuscripts, microfilms, and originals of local newspapers, oral history tapes, and research files, which are available for use on the premises, under supervision.

Activities
Guided tours through the keeper's home

Admission
Entry fee.
Displays: open Monday–Saturday, 10 A.M.–4 P.M., May–September.
Lighthouse: open Wednesday–Sunday, 10 A.M.–4 P.M., May–October.

DANA POINT
Nautical Heritage Museum

The Nautical Heritage Museum
24532 Del Prado Street
Dana Point, CA 92629
(714) 661-1001

Location
Dana Point is on I-5 four miles north of San Clemente. Exit at Dana Point onto Del Prado Street.

Highlights
The *Californian* (1848 revenue cutter)
The *Virginia* (1913 Q-boat)
Ship models
Paintings
Points of the Compass (newsletter)
Library

General Information
The Nautical Heritage Museum was established in 1981 to display museum-quality ship models, historic maritime documents, nautical artifacts, and paintings. Visitors can view elegantly encased models ranging from six inches to six feet in length. These include the USS *Constitution,* the clipper ship *Sea Witch,* and the *Mayflower*. Authentic documents from Abraham Lincoln, George Washington, and Thomas Jefferson, plus other significant pieces, are displayed.

The museum is owned by the National Heritage Society, which owns and operates the *Californian,* a 145-foot topsail gaff schooner christened in 1984 and used as a training ship for the youth of California. She is a re-creation of the *C. W. Lawrence*, an 1848 revenue cutter that patrolled the California coast during the 1850 Gold Rush.

Activities
Sea Scout and small-craft sailing instruction, research in *Q*-class and Chula Vista One-design vessels

Admission
No entry fee. Open Monday–Friday, 10 A.M.–4 P.M., year-round. Other times by appointment.

LONG BEACH
Queen Mary

Queen Mary/Spruce Goose
Pier J
P.O. Box 8
Long Beach, CA 90801
(213) 435-3511

Location
Long Beach is south of Los Angeles on I-405. The permanently moored *Queen Mary* can be approached via Queen's Way Bridge or Long Beach Freeway. Follow signs to Pier J in Long Beach Harbor.

Highlights
The *Queen Mary* (passenger ship)
Hall of Maritime Heritage
Gift shop

General Information
The *Queen Mary* was established as a tourist attraction, including the Hall of Maritime Heritage, in 1971. A retired British liner with 365 staterooms, salons, four restaurants, shops, a wedding chapel, and convention accommodations and meeting facilities, she is one of the largest passenger liners ever built.

The ship's collections include art deco architecture, fifty-six varieties of wood, acid-etched glass, memorabilia from the '30s and '40s, two 40,000-horsepower engines and power train, and small living quarters restored to show the *Queen* when she served as a military transport during World War II.

The Hall of Maritime Heritage features a gigantic model (weighing more than a ton) of the *Queen Mary,* a model of the *Mauretania,* navigational equipment, and a special exhibit called "Ships of Destiny" featuring a model of the ill-fated *Titanic.*

Activities
Self-guided tours include the bridge, officers' quarters, engine room, and upper decks. A variety of shops are also on board.

Note: Adjacent to the *Queen Mary* is the famous Howard Hughes flying boat *Spruce Goose,* which may likewise be toured.

Admission
Entry fee. Open daily, 10 A.M.–6 P.M., year-round.

MONTEREY

Allen Knight Maritime Museum

Allen Knight Maritime Museum
550 Calle Principal
P.O. Box 805
Monterey, CA 93942
(408) 375-2553

Location
Monterey is ninety miles south of San Francisco on the Pacific coastline via SR-1. Exit to center city.

Highlights
The *San Diego* (Vizcaino's ship)
Fresnel lens from the Point Sur Lighthouse
Ship models
Scrimshaw
Maritime library (2,000 volumes)

General Information

Portraying the sailing-ship era—the fishing and whaling days in Monterey—and local naval history (1846), the Allen Knight Maritime Museum opened in January 1971 to exhibit a large private collection of maritime artifacts and relics accumulated by the late Allen Knight of Carmel, California. His lifelong devotion to ships and the sea began when he served as a young deckhand on the sailing ship *Falls of Clyde,* which is now restored and moored at the Hawaii Maritime Center in Honolulu.

The Knight museum portrays the fishing and whaling era in Monterey and local naval history. Collections include sailing-ship models, steering wheels, bells, blocks, compasses, lanterns, scrimshaw, navigation instruments, ship name boards and other parts of old ships, and prints and paintings of ships.

Special features include the ship *San Diego,* captained by the Spanish explorer Vizcaino, who had followed Juan Rodriguez Cabrillo in his California coastal exploration in 1542. Another special feature is a beautiful large model of the frigate *Savannah,* the flagship of Commodore John Drake Sloat when he captured Monterey in 1846.

A comprehensive maritime library, including many volumes of old *Lloyd's Register,* is available primarily for researchers, writers, scholars, and artists.

Activities

Guided tours and lectures

Admission

No entry fee, but donations accepted. Memberships are available. Open Tuesday–Friday, 10 A.M.–4 P.M., Saturday and Sunday, 2 P.M.–4 P.M., June–September; Tuesday–Friday, 1 P.M.–4 P.M., Saturday and Sunday, 2 P.M.–4 P.M., October–May. Closed national holidays.

NEWPORT BEACH
Newport Beach Nautical Museum

Newport Beach Nautical Museum
1714 West Balboa Boulevard
Newport Beach, CA 92661
(619) 673-3377

Location
Newport Beach is south of Long Beach on I-405. Exit onto SR-55 west to Newport Beach. Follow Newport Boulevard, which becomes Balboa Boulevard, onto the Balboa peninsula just south of Newport Beach.

Highlights
Maritime history

General Information
Founded in 1983, Newport Beach Nautical Museum was established to preserve the nautical heritage of and maritime information about Newport Harbor.

Admission
Call or write the museum for information about opening hours.

OXNARD
Ventura County Maritime Museum

Ventura County Maritime Museum
1645 Pacific Avenue, #107
Oxnard, CA 93033
(619) 486-9867

Location
Oxnard is north of Los Angeles on the southern end of the Santa Barbara Channel. Take Rte. 101 to the Vineyard exit, then head south to Oxnard Boulevard. Travel four miles to Channel Islands Boulevard. The museum is approximately two miles west of the intersection of Channel Islands Boulevard and Victoria.

Highlights
Ship models
Maritime paintings

General Information
The Ventura County Maritime Museum, founded in 1989, is a recreational, educational, and research facility whose theme is "Sailing—Past, Present, and Future." The museum contains information about the Channel Islands, including Juan Rodriguez Cabrillo, the discoverer of California, who died here and is buried on one of the islands. The museum also brings to life the shipwrecks and maritime adventures of the Channel Islands.

Admission
The museum opened in the summer of 1990. Call or write for information about their opening hours.

PACIFIC GROVE
Point Pinos Lighthouse

Point Pinos Lighthouse
Keeper of the Light
1081 Herders Road
Pebble Beach, CA 93953
(408) 375-4450

Location
Pacific Grove is just west of Monterey in north central California, or 123 miles south of San Francisco. Pass through Monterey and Pacific Grove, heading west to the end of Lighthouse Avenue.

Highlights
Point Pinos Lighthouse

General Information
Point Pinos (point of pines) Lighthouse is the oldest continuously operating lighthouse on the West Coast. A small maritime museum is housed there.

Admission
No entry fee. Open Saturdays and Sundays only, 1 P.M.–4 P.M. Closed 22, 23, 29, and 30 December. For special tours, phone ahead.

PORT HUENEME
Civil Engineer Corps/Seabee Museum

CEC/Seabee Museum
Commodore B. W. Fink, Jr. Building (99)
Naval Construction Battalion Center
Port Hueneme, CA 93043-5000
(805) 982-5163

Location
From Oxnard (northwest of Los Angeles) take Rte. 101 to the SR-1 south exit. Follow signs to the Naval Construction Battalion Center in Port Hueneme (pronounced Y-NE-ME).

Highlights
Keepsakes from countries and islands Seabees have visited
Dioramas depicting Seabee construction feats
Unusual hunting and farming implements
Gift shop

General Information
The Civil Engineer Corps/Seabee Museum, founded in 1947, is a lasting monument to the history and fighting spirit of the Seabees and Naval Civil Engineer Corps. The museum contains numerous artifacts such as weapons, swords, unusual hunting and farming implements, and personal memorabilia relating to the customs and cultures of the various countries and islands where Seabees have served and are still serving. It also features dioramas that depict some of the Seabees' larger construction feats.

Admission
No entry fee. Open Monday–Friday, 8 A.M.–5 P.M., Saturday, 9 A.M.–4:30 P.M., and Sunday, 12:30 P.M.–4:30 P.M. Closed national holidays.

SAN DIEGO
Cabrillo National Monument

Cabrillo National Monument Memorial
1800 Cabrillo Memorial Drive
San Diego, CA 92106
(619) 557-5450

Location
Overlooking the city and harbor, at the south end of Cabrillo Memorial Drive (SR-209), the monument sits atop Point Loma Peninsula, west of downtown San Diego.

Highlights
Old Point Loma Lighthouse
Gray whale observation point
Statue of Juan Rodriguez Cabrillo

General Information
Cabrillo National Monument is approached through the gates of the Naval Ocean Systems Center. A statue commemorates Juan Rodriguez Cabrillo, who first landed near here in 1542. The historic lighthouse, first lit in 1855, served passing ships for nearly forty years.

The overlook provides a point from which to observe the annual gray whale migrations (December–February). Recorded interpretations are at the lighthouse and whale overlook. A Visitor's Center features exhibits on Cabrillo's voyage and films.

Activities
Various audiovisual and gray whale programs

Admission
Entry fee. Open daily, 10 A.M.–4 P.M., year-round.

Maritime Museum of San Diego

Maritime Museum Association of San Diego
1306 North Harbor Drive
San Diego, CA 92101
(619) 234-9153

Location
This floating museum on board three ships is located in downtown San Diego on the colorful Embarcadero.

Highlights
The *Star of India* (1863 bark)
The *Berkeley* (1898 ferry)
The *Medea* (1904 steam yacht)
Ship models
Mains'l Haul (periodical)
Library

General Information
Founded in 1948, the Maritime Museum of San Diego features three historic ships that represent both sail and steam power. Visitors can step back into history to view fine craftsmanship, life at sea, steam engines, naval history, demonstrations of maritime skills, and an interesting variety of exhibits for all ages. Collections include historic ships, small crafts, ship models, navigation instruments, luxury-liner memorabilia, tools, photographs, U.S. Navy artifacts, marine engineering, and pleasure boats.

Activities
Guided tours, speakers bureau, lectures, films, and demonstrations

Admission
Entry fee. Memberships are available. Open daily, 9 A.M.–8 P.M., year-round.

SAN FRANCISCO

San Francisco Maritime National Historical Park

San Francisco Maritime National Historical Park
Fort Mason Building 201
San Francisco, CA 94123
(415) 556-3002
Hyde Street: (415) 556-6435
J. Porter Shaw Library: (415) 556-9870
Historic Documents: (415) 556-9876

Location
The maritime park lies at the foot of Polk and Hyde streets in Aquatic Park, on the north shore of San Francisco. It's just west of Fisherman's Wharf, across from Ghirardelli Square.

Highlights
Boardable national historic landmark vessels
Maritime artifacts and ship models
Marine paintings
Scrimshaw
J. Porter Shaw Library and archives
Hyde Street Pier

General Information
Founded in 1951, San Francisco Maritime National Historical Park has displays on West Coast maritime history from the 1800s to the present. Collections include: 250,000 photographs and negatives of ships and shipping ports; 120,000 sheets of ship plans; 3,000 logbooks and 5,000 charts; manuscripts; scrimshaw and fine art; ship models; 142,000 books, periodicals, and oral histories of seafaring men and shipowners; artifacts from historic vessels; steam machinery; and small craft.

Historic ships on Hyde Street Pier include: the *Balclutha,* a 301-foot square-rigged ship; the *C. A. Thayer,* a 219-foot lumber schooner; *Eureka,* a side-wheel walking-beam ferry; the *Alma,* a 59-foot scow schooner (1891); the *Eppleton Hall,* a paddlewheel tug/Monterey fishing boat; the *Hercules,* a 150-foot steam tug (1907); and the *Wapama,* a steam schooner, which is located at the

U.S. Army Corps of Engineers' Sausalito waterfront at the Bay Model Visitor's Center.

The *Hercules,* a steam tug, is moored at Pier 1's Fort Mason Center (not associated with the park). Pier 43 houses the national liberty ship *Jeremiah O'Brien.* And currently located at Pier 39, just east of the museum and Fisherman's Wharf, is the submarine USS *Pampanito.*

Activities
Lectures, special tours, small-boat restoration program, films, changing exhibits, boatbuilding classes, and sea music programs

Admission
Museum: no entry fee. Open daily, 10 A.M.–6 P.M., May–October; 10 A.M.–5 P.M., November–April.

J. Porter Shaw Library: no entry fee. Open Thursday and Friday, 1 P.M.–5 P.M., Saturday, 10 A.M.–5 P.M., year-round.

Hyde Street Pier: entry fee. Open daily, 10 A.M.–5 P.M., November–April; 10 A.M.–6 P.M., May–October.

Treasure Island Museum

Treasure Island Museum
Building 1, Treasure Island
San Francisco, CA 94130
(415) 765-6182

Location
Treasure Island, between San Francisco and Oakland, is entered from the Oakland Bay Bridge (I-80 east/west).

Highlights
Marine, naval, U.S. Coast Guard, and China clipper flying boat history
Library

General Information
The Treasure Island Museum was established in 1975 as a temporary exhibit to commemorate the U.S. Navy and the Marine Corps

The *California*—one of the 1930s bait boats used in the Pacific to assist tuna boats based out of San Diego. Like "mother ships" to take on the day's catch, the bait boats were always available to supply the hardworking fishermen with needed bait. (Photo: Jerry MacMullen Library, Maritime Museum of San Diego.)

during the Bicentennial. In 1976 the two services converted the temporary exhibit into a permanent museum. In 1981 the Coast Guard joined the museum, making it the only museum in the country devoted to the history of all three sea services.

The museum's collections focus first on 1813, the year the frigate *Essex*—America's first naval ship in the Pacific—rounded Cape Horn. They move on, then, to: original documents and lithographs from Commodore Perry's expedition to Japan in 1854; the lighthouse lens from the Farallon Islands (twenty-seven miles west of San Francisco), made in France around 1850; uniforms and photographs dating from the Marine Corps intervention in the Boxer Rebellion in China (1899); souvenirs of the Great White Fleet visit to San Francisco in May 1908; photographs and souvenirs of the 1939/40 Golden Gate International Exposition (for which the island was created); a large model of the original China clipper flying boats, based on the island from 1939 to 1946; uniforms and weaponry from World War II; and relics of the all-navy Apollo XII moon mission.

Other permanent exhibits include "Pacific Panorama," which highlights major events in the history of sea services in the Pacific, and "Sovereigns of the Sea: The American Battleship in the Pacific."

Activities
Guided tours, organization meetings, and films

Admission
No entry fee. Open daily, 10 A.M.–3:30 P.M., year-round.

SAN PEDRO
Los Angeles Maritime Museum

Los Angeles Maritime Museum
Berth 84 at the Foot of 6th Street
San Pedro, CA 90731
(213) 548-7618

Location
San Pedro is west of Long Beach on the San Pedro Channel. The museum is immediately north of the Ports of Call Village in Berth 84 of the old Ferry Building at the foot of 6th Street.

Highlights
Ship models
Naval and marine history
Maritime art
The Compass Rose (newsletter)

General Information
The Los Angeles Maritime Museum displays historical photographs of Los Angeles harbor and assorted hardware and equipment from the USS *Los Angeles*. It also houses a twenty-one-foot scale model of the *Queen Mary* and a cutaway eighteen-foot scale model of both the *Titanic* and the *Lusitania*.

Activities
Daily tours by prior appointment

Admission
No entry fee, but donations accepted. Open Tuesday–Sunday, 10 A.M.–5 P.M., year-round.

HAWAII

HONOLULU
USS *Arizona* Memorial

United States Ship *Arizona* Memorial
1 Arizona Memorial Place
Honolulu, HI 96818
(808) 422-2771

Location
The memorial is in Pearl Harbor, adjacent to Honolulu on the island of Oahu. Take I-H1 to State Highway 99, following signs to the navy's Visitor's Center.

Highlights
The USS *Arizona* Memorial
Research library

General Information
The USS *Arizona* Memorial, founded in 1980, exhibits items that relate to: the history of wartime Hawaii and Japanese attacks on Oahu's military sites; the salvage and repair of ships; and the administrative history of the development of the cemetery and memorial.

A research library relating to Pearl Harbor and World War II is available for use on the premises through advance appointments. Videotaped programs are also available.

Activities
Guided programs, shuttle boat to the memorial, lectures, a film, and educational programs

Admission
No entry fee. Visitor's Center: open daily, 7:30 A.M.–5 P.M., year-round.

Boat trip to the memorial: open daily, 8 A.M.–3 P.M., closed Thanksgiving, Christmas, and New Year's Day.

Bishop Museum

Bishop Museum
1525 Bernice Street
P.O. Box 19000-A
Honolulu, HI 96817
(808) 647-3511

Location
East of downtown Honolulu, the museum is on Bernice Street off Rte. 63.

Highlights
Planetarium
Ship models
Library (90,000 volumes)
Gift shop

General Information
Bishop Museum was founded in 1889 and is famous for its extensive array of Pacific cultural and economic artifacts. The planetarium shows illustrate the Polynesians' navigational abilities that enabled them to sail great distances to the north, settling in the area first known as the Sandwich Islands and now known as Hawaii.

In its extensive collections, the museum also contains several small but important exhibits in honor of the mariner, a depiction of the freighter/passenger business, a small whaling exhibit, and an exhibit of ocean voyaging in ancient Polynesia.

Activities
Lectures, films, and education programs

Admission
Entry fee. Memberships are available. Open daily, 9 A.M.–5 P.M., year-round.

USS *Bowfin* (Submarine)

USS *Bowfin* (SS 287)
Near Ford Island Ferry
Honolulu, HI 96860
(808) 423-1341

Location
The submarine is docked at the USS *Arizona* Memorial in Honolulu, on the island of Oahu. Take I-H1 to State Highway 99, following signs to the navy's Visitor's Center.

Highlights
World War II submarine

General Information
The USS *Bowfin* (SS 287) is a privately maintained memorial to World War II submariners, the men of the "Silent Service." Commissioned on 1 May 1943, the *Bowfin* performed with distinction in the Pacific. After serving as a reserve training ship in the 1960s, she was saved from the scrap heap and restored by the Pacific Fleet Submarine Memorial Association. A self-guided tour of the boat is aided by wireless radio receivers, complete with sound effects. Attendants are on hand to ensure safety and to answer questions.

Admission
Entry fee. Open daily, 9:30 A.M.–5 P.M., year-round. Closed Thanksgiving, Christmas, and New Year's Day.

Hawaii Maritime Center

Hawaii Maritime Center
Pier 7, Honolulu Harbor
Honolulu, HI 96813
(808) 536-6801

Location
The center is on Pier 7, off of Ala Moana Boulevard, at Honolulu harbor near the downtown area.

Highlights
The *Falls of Clyde* (sailing ship)
The *Hokule'a* (Polynesian double-hull voyaging canoe)
Pier 7 (international steamship pier)
Aloha Tower Visitor's Center
Kalakaua Boathouse on Pier 7

General Information
The Hawaii Maritime Center was established in 1984 and comprises several indoor and outdoor displays that illustrate the maritime history of Honolulu's harbor.

The Kalakaua Boathouse, a world-class maritime museum, was opened 16 November 1988, the birthdate of the museum's namesake, King David Kalakaua. The 25,000-square-foot museum houses an extensive collection of marine and maritime exhibits, a multipurpose room, a restaurant, and other public areas.

The *Falls of Clyde,* a four-masted sailing ship, was built in 1878 at Port Glasgow, Scotland. Joining her is the *Hokule'a,* a Polynesian voyaging canoe that successfully demonstrates the Polynesians' venerable ability to navigate without instruments.

Admission
Entry fee. Open daily, 9 A.M.–5 P.M., year-round.

Pacific Submarine Museum

Pacific Submarine Museum
11 Arizona Memorial Drive
Pearl Harbor, HI 96860
(808) 471-0632

Location
The museum is in Honolulu on the naval submarine base off the Nimitz Highway. Take State Highway 99 off I-H1 to Makalapa Gate and North Road.

Highlights
The USS *Parche* conning tower
Japanese one-man submarine
Library (1,500 volumes)

General Information
Founded in 1970, the Pacific Submarine Museum contains documents and memorabilia relating to the "Silent Service." Exhibits include the conning tower and superstructure of the USS *Parche,* a Japanese one-man suicide sub, and a model of a nuclear-powered submarine. Collections include submarine memorabilia, assorted missile and torpedo displays, navigation systems, World War II patrol reports, files on submarines since 1900, publications on submarines, and an A-2 Polaris missile.

Activities
Guided tours, presentations and lectures, and education programs

Admission
No entry fee. Identification must be presented at the Nimitz Main Gate to obtain a pass. Open Wednesday–Sunday, 9:30 A.M.–5 P.M., year-round.

MAUI

Carthaginian II Floating Museum

Carthaginian II Floating Museum
At-the-Dock
Lahaina, HI 96761
(808) 661-8527/3262 (Lahaina Restoration Foundation)

Location
The museum is at Lahaina, on the island of Maui.

Highlights
Square-rigged brig
Humpback whale presentation
Library (500 volumes)

General Information
Carthaginian II Floating Museum is a 120-foot two-masted, square-rigged brig of the type that bore the first missionaries around Cape Horn from New England to Lahaina. A nineteenth-century whaling dory, as well as artifacts and pictures from the whaling era, are displayed. An audiovisual presentation featuring humpback whales is also shown.

Activities
Guided tours, lectures, films, and exhibitions

Admission
Entry fee. Memberships are available. Open daily, 9 A.M.–4 P.M., year-round.

WAIMANALO
Pacific Whaling Museum

Pacific Whaling Museum
Sea Life Park
Scenic Route 72
Waimanalo, HI 96795
(808) 259-5177

Location
On the island of Oahu, Waimanalo is south of Kailua via SR-72. The museum is in Sea Life Park on Waimanalo Bay.

Highlights
Scrimshaw
Library (100 volumes)

General Information
Founded in 1979, the Pacific Whaling Museum contains a large collection of whaling artifacts from the Golden Era of whaling. Visitors will discover the finest in scrimshaw work, maritime tools, harpoons, and a full sperm whale skeleton.

Admission
No entry fee. Open daily, 9:30 A.M.–4:30 P.M., year-round.

APPENDIX

CANAL PARKS

LISTED BELOW ARE THE NAMES OF SELECTED CANAL PARKS. FOR MORE INFORMATION ABOUT A SPECIFIC PARK, PLEASE WRITE TO THE FOLLOWING:

The American Canal Society
117 Main Street
Freemansburg, PA 18017

or **Virginia Canals and Navigation Society**
6826 Rosemont Drive
McLean, VA 22101

Albemarle and Chesapeake Canal (Great Bridge, VA)
Alexandria Canal Tide Lock Park (Alexandria, VA)
Armory Canal (Harper's Ferry, WV)
Battery Creek Lock Restoration (Near Lynchburg, VA)
Ben Salem Lock Wayside (Between Lexington and Buena Vista, VA)
Big Sandy Lock and Dam 3 (Louisa, KY, and Fort Gay, WV)
Black River Canal (NY)
Blackstone Canal (MA)
Cayuga-Seneca Canal (NY)
Champlain Canal (NY)
Chemung Canal (NY)
Chenango Canal (NY)
Chessie Nature Trail (Lexington, VA)
Crofton Lock (Near Charlottesville, VA)
Deep Creek Lock Park (Deep Creek, VA)
Delaware and Raritan Canal (NJ/PA)
Dismal Swamp Canal (Deep Creek, VA, and South Mills, NC)
Eagle Rock Lock Park (Eagle Rock, VA)
Fredericksburg Canal (Fredericksburg, VA)
Genesee Valley Canal (NY)
Goose Creek State Scenic River (Loudoun County, VA)
Great Dismal Swamp National Wildlife Refuge (Deep Creek, VA, and South Mills, NC)
Great Falls Park (VA)
Great Ship Lock Park (Richmond, VA)
Hocking Canal (OH)
Humpback Bridge Wayside Park (Near Covington, VA)

Kanawha River Navigation (Winfield, Marmet, and London, WV)
Lehigh Navigation (PA)
Little Kanawha River Navigation (Leachtown, WV)
Louisville and Portland (KY)
Marmet Park (Near Charleston, WV)
Miami and Erie Canal (OH)
Monongahela River Navigation (Morgantown, Hildebrand, and Opekiska, WV and PA)
New Haven and Northampton (CT)
New River Gorge National River (Hinton and Fayetteville, WV)
Ohio and Pennsylvania Canal (OH)
Ohio River Navigation (WV Border)
Old Dominion Railway Transportation Museum (Richmond, VA)
Palmyra Lock (Palmyra, VA)
Patowmack Canal (Great Falls, VA)
Rappahannock State Scenic River (Fauquier County, VA)
Rivanna State Scenic River (Fluvanna County, VA)
Roanoke Canal Locks (Roanoke Rapids, NC)
Sandy and Beaver Canal (OH)
Santee and Cooper Canal (SC)
Schuylkill Navigation (Philadelphia, PA)
Shenandoah Canal (Harper's Ferry, WV)
Shenandoah State Scenic River (Clarke County, VA)
Staunton State Scenic River (Between Long Island and Brookneal, VA)
Susquehanna and Tidewater (PA)
Tidewater Connection Locks Park (Richmond, VA)
Union Mills Canal Towpath Trail (Lake Monticello, VA)
Upper Appomattox Canal (Petersburg, VA)
Upper James State Scenic River (Botetourt County, VA)
Wabash and Erie Canal (IN)
Whitewater Canal (IN)

NAME INDEX

SUBJECT INDEX

BED AND BREAKFAST

BOATBUILDING

BOAT MODELS

CANALS

CHANTY SINGING

GIFT SHOPS

HALLS OF FAME

HOSTELS

LIBRARIES

LIGHTHOUSES/ LIGHTSHIPS

LOCKS AND CANALS

NAVY YARDS

NEWSLETTERS

SCRIMSHAW

SHIP CHANDLERIES

SHIP MODELS

SHIPS/BOATS

WHALING

WOODEN BOATS

A NOTE TO MUSEUM DIRECTORS

An effort was made to include all the maritime museums in North America, but in all likelihood some were missed. If you'd like a listing for your museum in the next edition, please complete the form below.

The following maritime museum was not included in this guide:

____

(Name of museum, lighthouse, canal museum)

____

(Street address and Post Office Box number)

____

(City/State/Zip or Canadian Mail Code)

____

(Phone number[s])

This museum is important because:

____

____

____

Please send to: Naval Institute Press
Attention: Robert H. Smith
United States Naval Institute
Annapolis, MD 21402

Thank you.

ABOUT THE AUTHOR

ROBERT H. SMITH is a longtime supporter of marine and maritime philanthropies and the author of two popular guides to harbors, anchorages, and marinas in Northern and Southern California. Formerly, he was assistant to the chancellor of the University of California, San Diego (the home of Scripps Institution of Oceanography), and vice-president of development at a medical and research foundation in La Jolla, California.

The **Naval Institute Press** is the book-publishing arm of the U.S. Naval Institute, a private, nonprofit professional society for members of the sea services and civilians who share an interest in naval and maritime affairs. Established in 1873 at the U.S. Naval Academy in Annapolis, Maryland, where its offices remain today, the Naval Institute has more than 100,000 members worldwide.

Members of the Naval Institute receive the influential monthly magazine *Proceedings* and discounts on fine nautical prints, ship and aircraft photos, and subscriptions to the quarterly *Naval History* magazine. They also have access to the transcripts of the Institute's Oral History Program and get discounted admission to any of the Institute-sponsored seminars regularly offered around the country.

The Naval Institute's book-publishing program, begun in 1898 with basic guides to naval practices, has broadened its scope in recent years to include books of more general interest. Now the Naval Institute Press publishes more than forty new titles each year, ranging from how-to books on boating and navigation to battle histories, biographies, ship and aircraft guides, and novels. Institute members receive discounts on the Press's more than 375 books.

Full-time students are eligible for special half-price membership rates. Life memberships are also available.

For a free catalog describing the Naval Institute Press books currently available, and for further information about U.S. Naval Institute membership, please write to:

Membership & Communications Department
U.S. Naval Institute
Annapolis, Maryland 21402

Or call, toll-free, (800) 233-USNI. In Maryland, call (301) 224-3378.

THE NAVAL INSTITUTE PRESS

THE NAVAL INSTITUTE GUIDE TO MARITIME MUSEUMS OF NORTH AMERICA

Designed by R. Dawn Sollars

Set in Times Roman and Gill Sans
by TCSystems, Inc., Shippensburg, Pennsylvania

Printed on 50-lb. Glatfelter High Opaque vellum finish
and bound in Kivar
by The Maple-Vail Book Manufacturing Group,
York, Pennsylvania